HUMAN
6E ANATOMY
LABORATORY MANUAL

Steven Bassett

Mc Graw Hill Education

8 9 0 SCI SCI 17 16 15

ISBN-13: 978-0-07-813099-1
ISBN-10: 0-07-813099-9

Learning Solutions Consultant: Anni Schleicher
Project Manager: Mandy Maas
Cover Photo Credits: 102722843 – Sebastian Kaulitzki

TABLE OF CONTENTS

	Preface	
Chapter 1	Anatomical Terminology	1
Chapter 2	Cells and Tissues	13
Chapter 3	Overview of the Regions	36
Chapter 4A	Head and Neck: Skull	40
Chapter 4B	Head and Neck: Muscles	54
Chapter 4C	Head and Neck: Blood Vessels	59
Chapter 4D	Head and Neck: Nerves (Brain)	62
Chapter 5A	Upper Appendage: Bones	71
Chapter 5B	Upper Appendage: Muscles	81
Chapter 5C	Upper Appendage: Blood Vessels	90
Chapter 5D	Upper Appendage: Nerves	93
Chapter 5E	Upper Appendage: Joints	94
Chapter 6A	Lower Appendage: Bones	98
Chapter 6B	Lower Appendage: Muscles	109
Chapter 6C	Lower Appendage: Blood Vessels	121
Chapter 6D	Lower Appendage: Nerves	123
Chapter 6E	Lower Appendage: Joints	125

Chapter 7A	Torso: Bones	128
Chapter 7B	Torso: Muscles	135
Chapter $7C_1$	Torso: Heart	138
Chapter $7C_2$	Torso: Blood Vessels	145
Chapter 7D	Torso: Nerves (spinal cord)	148
Chapter 7E	Torso: Lungs	151
Chapter 7F	Torso: Abdominal organs	157
Chapter 8A	Pelvic Region: Urinary System	171
Chapter 8B	Pelvic Region: Male Reproduction	179
Chapter 8C	Pelvic Region: Female Reproduction	183
Chapter 9	Cranial Nerves	186
Chapter 10	The Ears	192
Chapter 11	The Eyes	199
	Assignments	209

First and foremost, I would like to thank my family (especially my wife) for putting up with me while I worked on this manual during the late hours of night and the wee hours of morning. My wife thinks I have a laptop computer attached to my body.

The terminology used in this lab manual is primarily based on Latin derivation. The lab manual strives to use the descriptive terms based on various medial dictionaries. Therefore, do not despair if you find there are two or three terms to describe a single part of, on, or within the body. The terms used in this manual are the proper anatomical terms rather than laymen's terms.

This lab manual is designed to teach anatomy from the regional approach. In other words, when studying the arm, you will study arm bones, arm muscles, arm nerves, and arm blood vessels.

At the end of each chapter is a listing of select terms used within that chapter. Along with the list of terms is the pronunciation. Your lab instructor will keep you up to date regarding the pronunciation as this is a continuous work in progress.

Toward the end of the manual, you will find a series of questions your instructor will assign to you.

CHAPTER 1   ANATOMICAL TERMINOLOGY

As you begin to explore the world of "proper anatomical terminology" you will find that most of the words are of Latin origin. Scientists use Latin because it is considered to be a dead language. Since Latin is a dead language, it is not commonly used in general conversation. Since it is not used in general conversation, it is not likely to be converted into slang.

Slang is usually only understood by those making up the slang and not understood by others. Since slang is understood by only small groups of people (in reference to the whole world) it can be very confusing to others. Some examples to illustrate the confusion resulting from the use of slang are:

- "That's a **bad** salad." The word "*bad*" among certain groups of people actually means *really good*.

- "I need to go to the **john**." Is this the same thing as needing to go and sit on the **porcelain pony** for a while or is it the same as "Wanting to see a man about a Wallaby?"

- "My rig has ten forward gears and a **Georgia overdrive**" How many people are familiar with a "*Georgia overdrive*"?

Latin is also a descriptive language. Common terminology usually is not descriptive. Some examples of descriptive terminology are:

- The tubes connected to the uterus are called **uterine tubes** rather than *Fallopian tubes.* The term Fallopian is derived from a person's name (Gabriele Faloppius). The use of the term *uterine tube* is understood to be a tube associated with the uterus.

- Our ear structure contains a **pharyngotympanic tube** (formerly called the *Eustachian tube*). The term Eustachian is derived from a person's name (Bartolomeo Eustachio). *Pharyngotympanic* refers to a tube that goes from the tympanic area of the ear to the pharyngeal area of the throat.

- The *Achilles' tendon* connects the gastrocnemius (calf) muscle to our heel bone. The proper anatomical term for this structure is **calcaneal tendon.** Achilles was a Greek mythological hero. The tendon connects the gastrocnemius muscle to our heel bone of which is called the calcaneus, hence, calcaneal tendon.

In order to understand the power of the descriptive nature of this language, you need to know the definition of these words. This knowledge comes with time. You will have a pretty good "handle" on it by the time you finish this course. In the meantime, **study, study,** and **study** some more! By the way, what does it mean to have a good "handle" on it?

Based on the previous information, you now know why scientists use those great, big multisyllabic words.

Exercise 1-1: Body Landmarks

1. Use your textbook to identify the following landmarks listed in table 1-1.

2. Figure 1-1 has leader lines pointing to landmarks we study in this course. You are to match the number (from table 1-1) with the appropriate leader line on the picture.

3. As you identify the landmarks via pictures, determine the approximate location of these landmarks on your body.

Table 1-1   Body Landmarks Used in This Class

	Head / Neck		Arms / Hand		Torso		Legs / Feet
1	Nasal	17	Brachium	30	Axilla	43	Femur
2	Otic	18	Antecubital	31	Thorax	44	Patella
3	Oris	19	Antebrachium	32	Abdomen	45	Crural
4	Ocular	20	Carpal	33	Umbilicus	46	Tarsal
5	Buccal	21	Pollex	34	Pelvis	47	Hallux
6	Frontal	22	Cubital (olecranon)	35	Inguinal	48	Popliteal
7	Mental	23		36	Dorsum of back	49	Sural
8	Cervical	24		37	Lumbar of back	50	Calcaneus
9	Occipital	25		38	Gluteus	51	
10	Zygomatic	26		39	Gluteal fold	52	
11	Temporal	27		40	Gluteal cleft	53	
12	Glabella	28		41	Iliac crest	54	
13	Nasion	29		42	mamma	55	
14	Ala of nose						
15	Nasolabial sulcus						
16	Vermillion border						

Figure 1-1   Body Landmarks

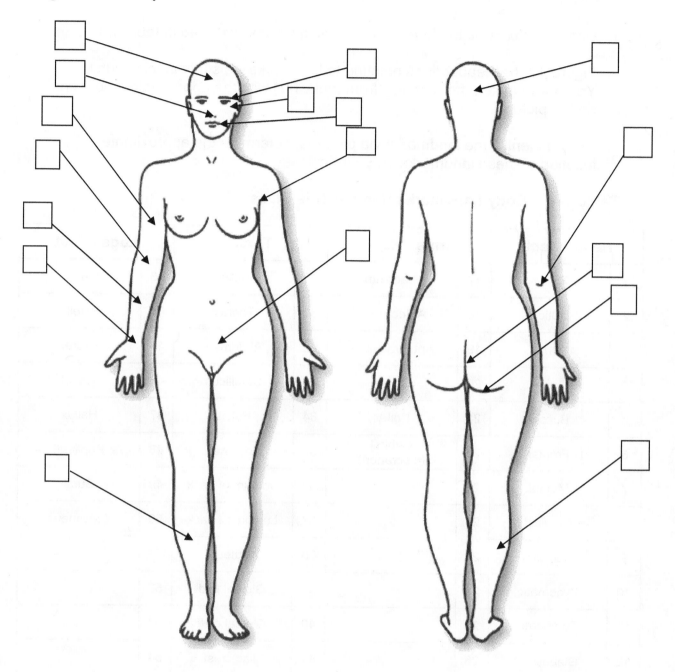

Figure 1-2   Body Landmarks

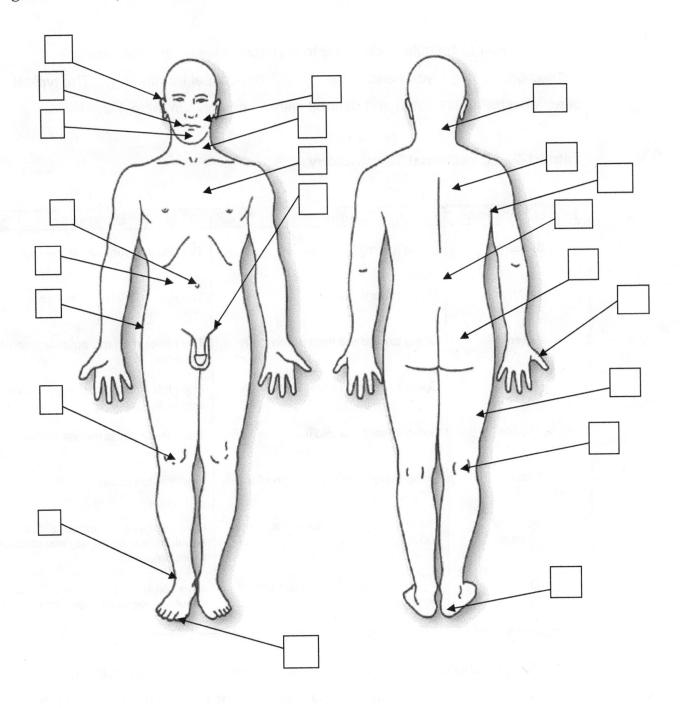

EXERCISE 1-2: DIRECTIONAL TERMINOLOGY

In order to be able to describe to someone else where something is located on the body, you need to use proper directional terminology. The typical directional terms are listed and defined with an example in table 1-2.

Table 1-2   Directional Terminology

Directional term	Definition	Example
Superior	Going toward the head	The nose is superior to the mouth.
Inferior	Going toward the feet	The chin is inferior to the nose.
Anterior	Going toward the front of the body	The navel is on the anterior side of the body.
Posterior	Going toward the back of the body	The gluteal cleft is on the posterior side of the body.
Medial	Going toward the midline of the body	The little finger is medial to the thumb.
Lateral	Going away from the midline of the body	The little toe is lateral to the hallux.
Proximal	The closest point to the trunk of the body	If we compare our elbow with our shoulder, we would say our shoulder is proximal.
Distal	The farthest point from the trunk of the body	If we compare our elbow with our shoulder, we would say our elbow is distal.

The directional terms listed above are useful only when we refer to the anatomical position of the body. In anatomy class, we will **always** refer to the body in the anatomical position (standing with the palms facing anterior).

Figure 1-3   Directional Terminology

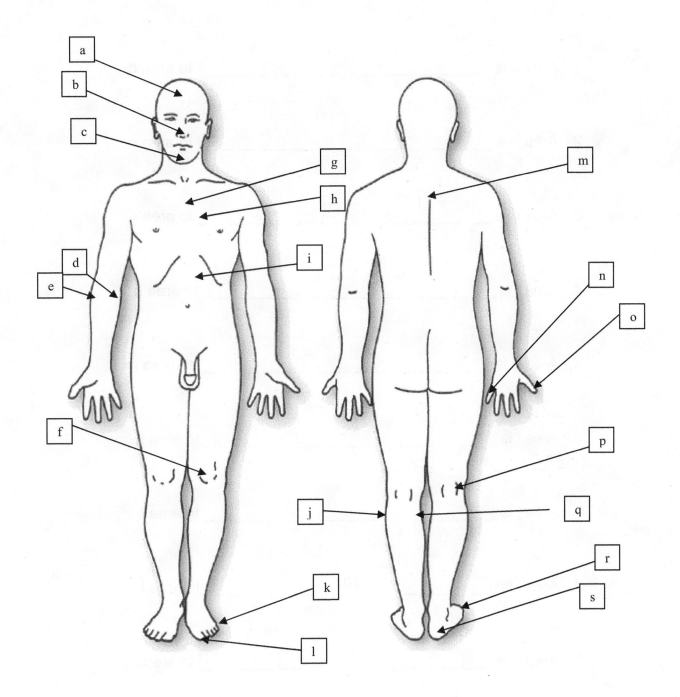

Use the terms in table 1-2 to fill in the blanks while viewing figure 1-3.

1. Area a is _____ to area b.

2. Area b is _____ to area c.

3. Area d is _____ to area e.

4. Area f is _____ to area p.

5. Area g is _____ to area m.

6. Area i is _____ to area h.

7. Area j is _____ to area q.

8. Area l is _____ to area k.

9. Area n is _____ to area o.

10. Area s is _____ to area r.

EXERCISE 1-3: DISSECTIONAL PLANES

In order to study the internal structures of the body, we need to make a **section** of the body. A section is made by cutting into the body. Each cut we make needs to be described in some manner so others, in future studies, can understand what we're doing. Anatomists typically use four planes; frontal plane, sagittal plane, transverse plane, and oblique plane. Look at table 1-4 for the description of the four planes and also look at pictures in your textbook that correspond to the information in table 1-4.

Table 1-4   Planes of Dissection

Dissectional Plane	Description
Sagittal plane	A dissectional cut that separates the body into left and right sections.
Frontal plane	A dissectional cut that separates the body into anterior and posterior sections.
Transverse plane	A dissectional cut that separates the body into superior and inferior sections.
Oblique plane	A dissectional cut that separates a piece of tissue at an angle.

In the lab room, you will find various models or organs, each of which has been cut into one of the four dissectional planes. Examine each specimen and determine the correct dissectional plane being represented. Put your answers in the blanks in the column identified as "Dissectional Planes."

Specimen	Dissectional Plane
A	_____
B	_____
C	_____
D	_____
E	_____
F	_____

EXERCISE 1-4: ABDOMINOPELVIC REGIONS

To help physicians "pinpoint" an ailment a patient might have, anatomists have divided the abdominal section into four quadrants and nine regions (abdominopelvic regions). Each quadrant and each region has specific organs associated with it.

Your lab instructor has "outlined" the abdominopelvic regions on a manikin in the lab room. Upon examination of the manikin, you will find numbered tags on select organs. You are to identify that organ within the specific abdominopelvic region and write it in table 1-5 below. There may be more than one tagged organ per abdominopelvic region.

Table 1-5   The Abdominopelvic Regions

Abdominopelvic Region	Organ Found in that Region
Epigastric	
Hypogastric	
Left Hypochondriac	
Right Hypochondriac	
Umbilical	
Left Inguinal	
Right Inguinal	
Left Lumbar	
Right Lumbar	

PRONUNCIATION

1	Antebrachium (an-tuh-bray-kee-um)		15	Hypogastric (high-poe-gas-trik)
2	Antecubital (an-tuh-que-bi-tul)		16	Inguinal (in-gwi-nul)
3	Axilla (aks-ill-uh)		17	Oblique (oh-bleek)
4	Brachium (bray-kee-um)		18	Occipital (ok-si-pi-tul)
5	Buccal (buh-kul)		19	Ocular (ok-you-lar)
6	Calcaneus (kal-cay-nee-us)		20	Olecranon (oh-lek-ruh-non)
7	Carpal (kar-pul)		21	Oris (or-iss)
8	Cervical (sir-vi-kul)		22	Otic (oh-tik)
9	Crural (krew-rul)		23	Pollex (paul-leks)
10	Cubital (que-bi-tul)		24	Popliteal (pop-li-tee-ul)
11	Epigastric (eh-pi-gas-trik)		25	Sagittal (saa-ji-tul)
12	Gluteus (glue-tee-us)		26	Sural (sir-ul)
13	Hallux (hal-uks)		27	Umbilicus (um-bi-lie-kus) (um-bil-i-kus)
14	Hypochondriac (high-poe-kon-dree-ak)		28	Zygomatic (zie-go-maa-tik)

CHAPTER 2   CELLS AND TISSUES

In this course we will study the various organ systems of the body by starting at the microscopic level and working our way to the macroscopic level. Anatomists have categorized the human body into various levels. The cellular level is the simplest of all the levels. A group of **cells** functioning together create the **tissue** level. A group of tissues functioning together will create an **organ**. Several organs functioning together create the **organ system**. All the organ systems functioning together create the **organism**.

There are about 75 trillion cells making up the human body. All of the 75 trillion cells can be placed into four major tissue categories. The four major tissues are; **epithelial, connective, muscular,** and **neural.** In order for the cells to be placed into one of the four categories they must exhibit certain characteristics.

1. All cells that **make up the inside or outside lining** of an organ are placed in the epithelial tissue category.
2. All cells that **have a matrix** belong in the connective tissue category.
3. All cells that **have the ability to contract** are placed in the muscular tissue category.
4. All cells that **transmit impulses** or provide protection for the cells that transmit impulses are placed in the neural tissue category.

Table 2-1 identifies the types of cells that can be found within each tissue category.

Every organ consists of several different kinds of cells belonging to different types of tissues. For example; the heart pushes blood cells through the body, which belong to the **connective tissue** category. The heart is lined by **epithelial tissue** consisting of squamous cells. The muscular portion of the heart consists of cardiac cells (**muscle tissue**). The heart beats rhythmically due to the activity of the pacemaker, which is a group of nerves (**neural tissue**), located in the right atrium of the heart.

13

Table 2-1   Tissue and Cell Types

Tissue	Cell Type (Studied in this class)
	**
Epithelial	Squamous (simple and stratified)
	Cuboidal (simple)
	Columnar (simple and pseudostratified)
	Transitional
	**
Connective	Adipose
	Areolar
	Blood
	Bone
	Cartilage
	Dense (regular, elastic, and irregular)
	Reticular
	**
Muscular	Skeletal
	Smooth
	Cardiac
	**
Neural	Neuron
	Glial (neuroglial cells)

EXERCISE 2-1 CELLS AND TISSUE IDENTIFICATION

On the lab tables are several microscopes. Each microscope will show a view of one of the cell types from table 2-1. Located around the room are photographs of the cell types from table 2-1. You are to look in each microscope, compare what you see to the corresponding picture in this manual (figures 2-1 through 2-14).   Then, examine the pictures that are in the lab room and determine what type of cell they represent. See exercise 2-2.

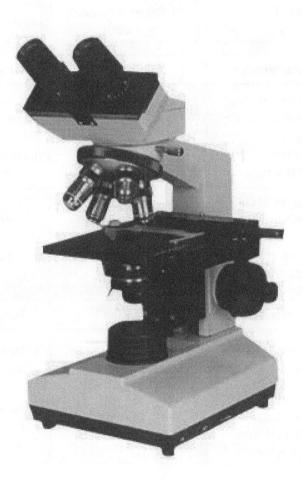

Table 2-2   Cell and Tissue Characteristics   (Epithelial Tissue)

	Characteristics	Location	Function	Other
Simple squamous	Single layer of flattened cells	Lines the alveolar sacs of the lungs. Lines the kidney glomeruli.	Cells are very permeable.	
Stratified squamous	Several layers of flattened cells	Lines the skin Lines the vagina Lines the esophagus Lines the mouth	Provides physical protection.	Deeper cells are either cuboid cells or columnar cells.
	Characteristics	**Location**	**Function**	**Other**
Simple columnar	Single layer of column-shaped cells. Nucleus is near the base of the cells.	Lines the GI tract. Lines the respiratory tubes. Lines the ovarian tubes.	Secrete and absorb material	Many columnar cells will have cilia.
Pseudostratified columnar	Single layer of cells of differing heights. Nuclei are at different levels.	Lines the trachea	Secrete and absorb material	Cilia move in such a manner to move mucus out of the trachea.
	Characteristics	**Location**	**Function**	**Other**
Simple cuboidal	Single layer of cube shaped cells.	Lines kidney tubules. Lines some glands	Secretion and absorption	The inside portion of the tube is called a lumen.
Transitional	Combination of stratified squamous, cuboidal, and columnar cells.	Lines the urinary bladder	Have the ability to stretch.	

Figure 2-1   Squamous cells

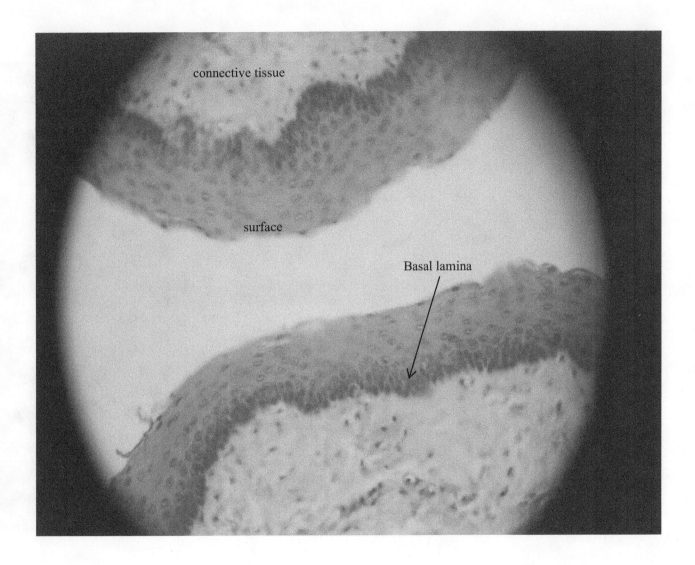

connective tissue

surface

Basal lamina

Figure 2-2   Columnar Cells

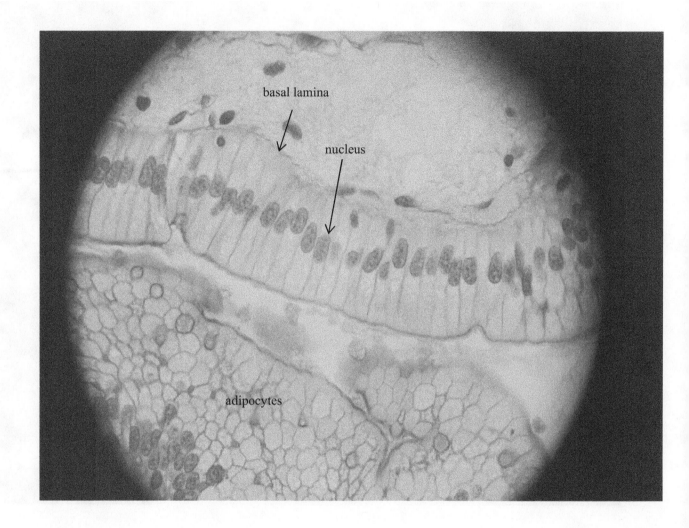

Figure 2-3   Cuboidal Cells

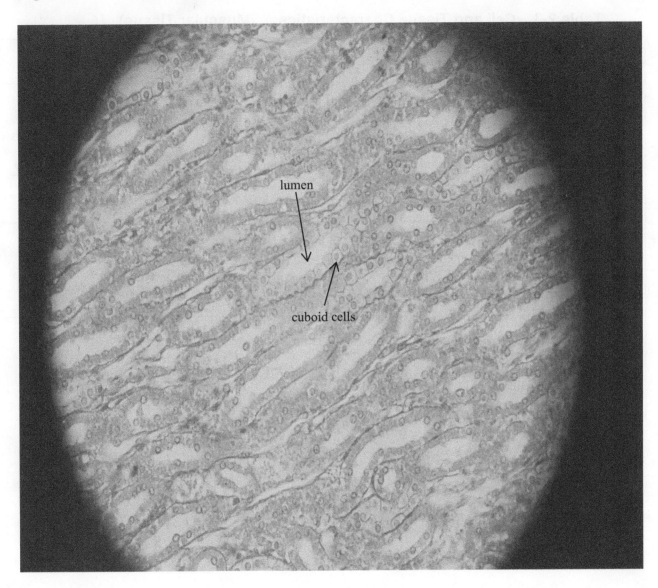

lumen

cuboid cells

Table 2-3 Cell and Tissue Characteristics (Muscular Tissue)

	Characteristics	Location	Function	Other
Skeletal muscle	Consists of overlapping fibers resulting in a stripes or striations. Consists of nuclei located near the edge of the fibers.	Muscles of the skeleton such as arm or leg muscles.	Voluntary contractions	A muscle fiber is the same thing as a muscle cell.
Smooth muscle	Consists of nuclei that have tapered ends.	Walls of the blood vessels, digestive organs, and uterus.	Involuntary contractions	Involved in peristaltic actions
Cardiac muscle	Visible striations or stripes. Consists of intercalated discs.	Only in the heart	Rhythmic contraction	Circulates the blood

Figure 2-4   Skeletal Muscle

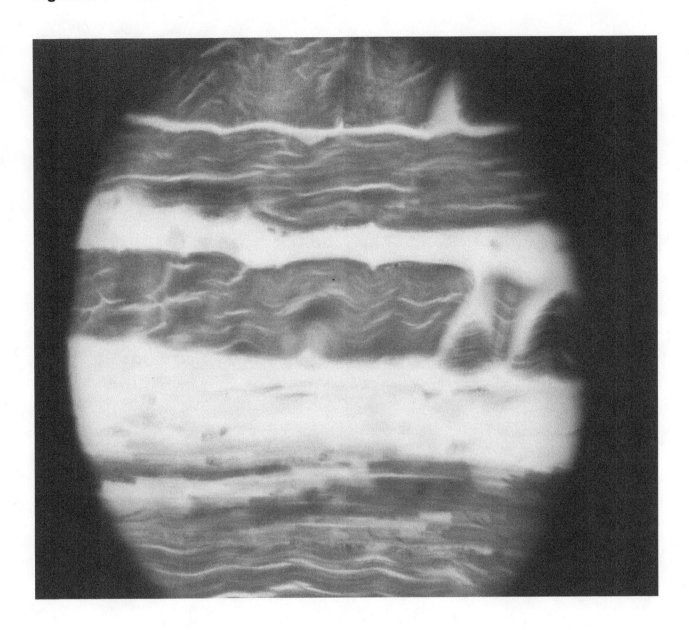

Figure 2-5   Cardiac Muscle

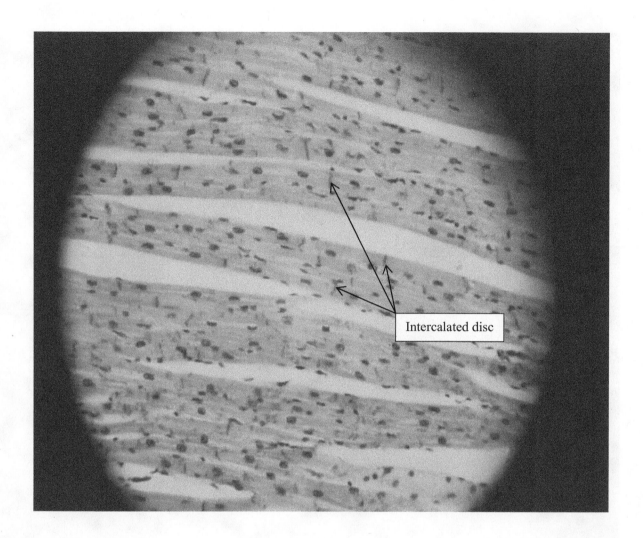

Intercalated disc

Figure 2-6   Smooth Muscle

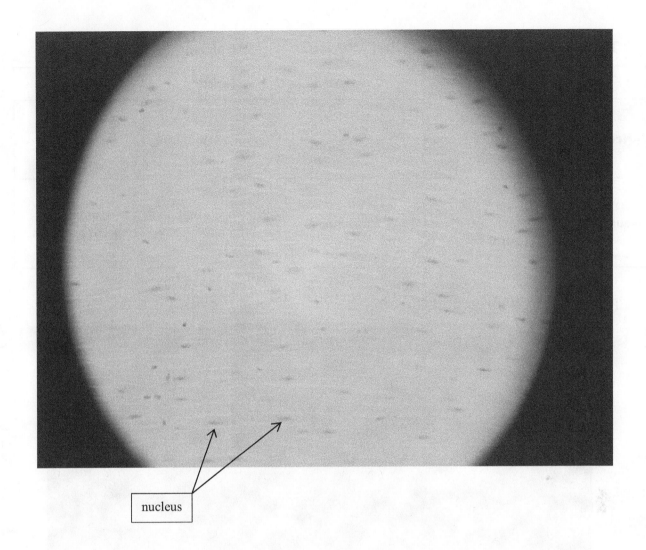

nucleus

Table 2-4   Cell and Tissue Characteristics   (Neural Tissue)

	Characteristics	Location	Function	Other
Neuron	Typically consists of a soma, dendrite, and an axon.	Throughout the nervous system	Conducts impulses	
Neuroglial	Many times will appear as specs located near the neurons.	Near the neuron or surrounding the axon.	Provides protection for the neuron.	There are many types of glial cells.

Figure 2-7   Neuron and Glial Cells

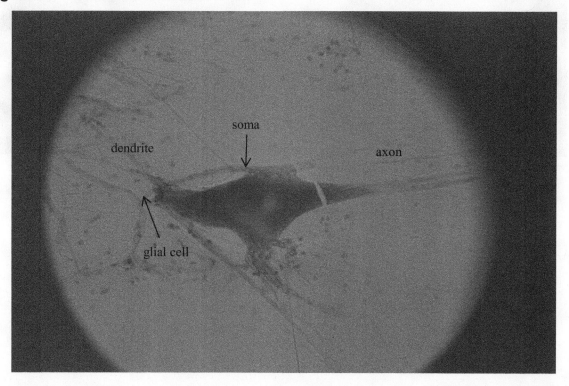

Table 2-5   Cell and Tissue Characteristics   (Connective Tissue)

	Characteristics	Location	Function	Other
Adipose tissue	Cells appear to be round and empty Matrix of fibers	Around organs	Provides insulation and a storage of energy	Cells are called adipocytes and are filled with molecules of fat.
Areolar tissue	Cells have lots of thin fibers passing between them. Matrix of fibers.	Found mainly between muscle and skin.	Literally connects skin to muscle.	Cellular components are called fibrocytes.

	Characteristics	Location	Function	Other
Dense Regular Tissue	Consists of fibers that are tightly packed together for strength. Matrix of fibers	Found in: tendons, ligaments, and aponeuroses.	Tendons: muscle to bone. Ligaments: bone to bone. Aponeuroses: typically muscle to muscle.	Consists of cells called fibrocytes, which generally cannot be seen due to the compactness of the fibers.
Reticular Tissue	Consists of an open framework of short, thick fibers. Matrix of fibers	Found in: Liver, spleen, tonsils, appendix, lymph nodes, and bone marrow.	Literally makes up the framework of the entire organ.	Consists of cells called fibrocytes.

Table 2-6   Cell and Tissue Characteristics   (Connective Tissue)

	Characteristics	Location	Function	Other
Blood tissue	Consists of small, round cells with space between them. Matrix of liquid called plasma.	Circulatory system	RBC: transports oxygen and carbon dioxide. WBC: fights infectious agents Platelets: blood clotting	RBC = erythrocyte WBC = leukocyte Thrombocytes = platelets
	Characteristics	**Location**	**Function**	**Other**
Bone Tissue	Osteocytes are arranged in a circular form. Matrix is a solid material (called lamellae)	Long bones of the skeleton.	Provides support for the body	Cells are called osteocytes Main functioning unit is an osteon.
Cartilage Tissue	Consists of small cells in a large lacuna, hence a white space around the cell. Matrix is a gel material.	Helix of the ear Between joints Ala of the nose	Provides flexibility Reduces friction within the joints	Cells are called chondrocytes.

Figure 2-8   Adipose

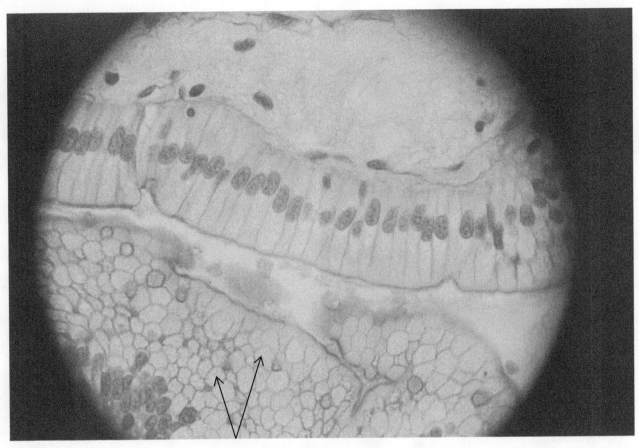

adipose

Figure 2-9   Areolar

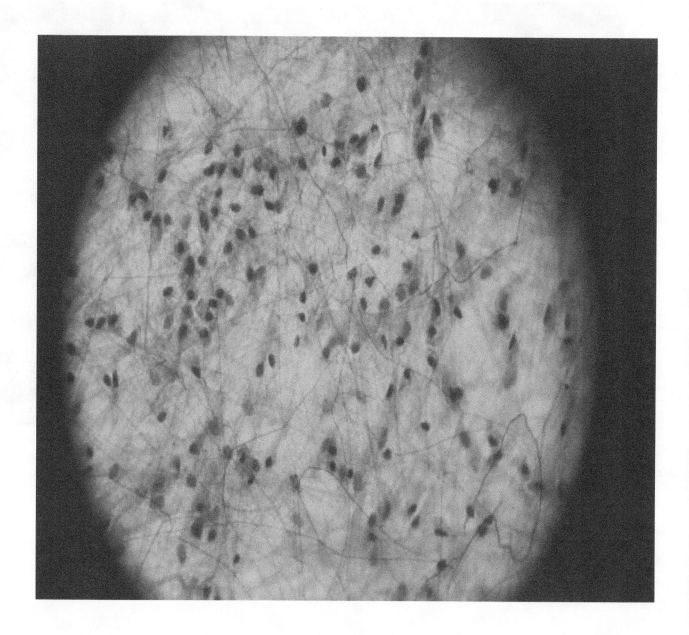

Figure 2-10   Dense

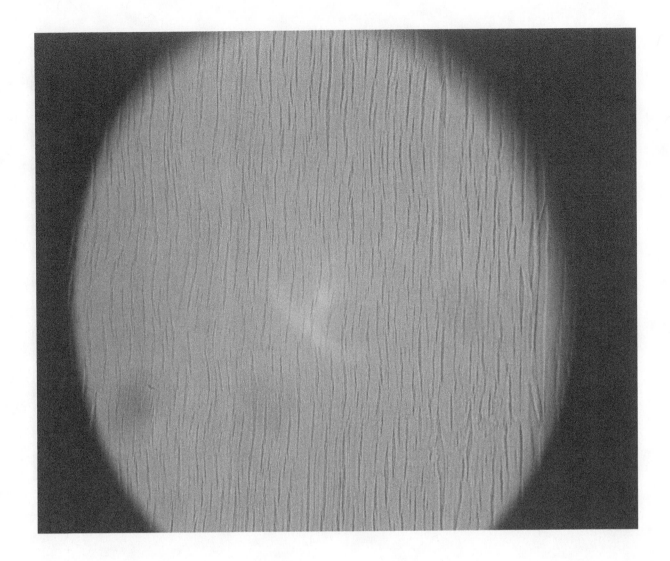

Figure 2-11   Reticular

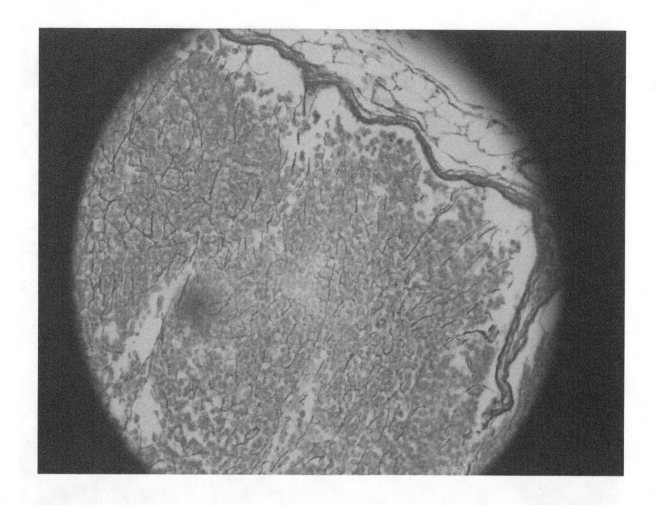

Figure 2-12   Blood

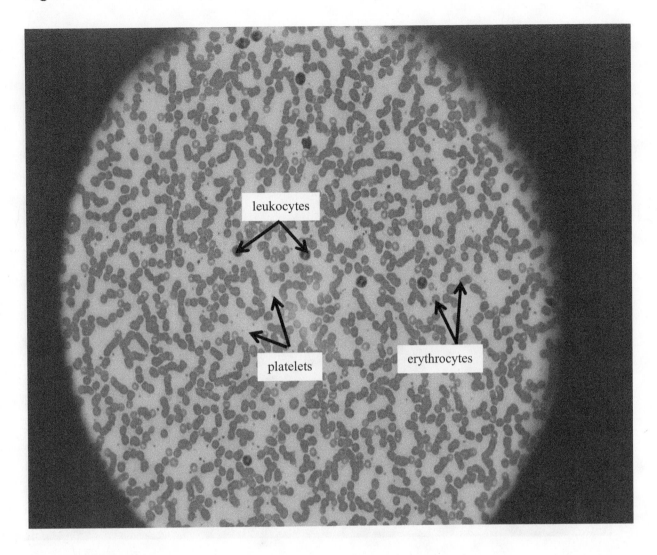

Figure 2-13   Bone

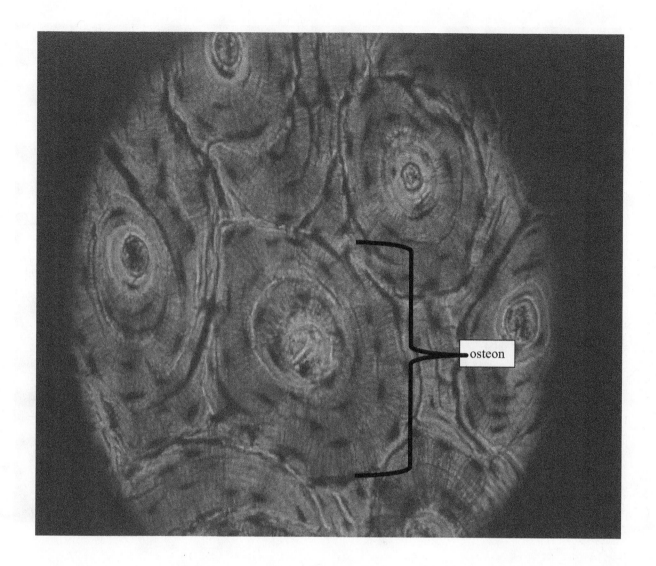

osteon

Figure 2-14   Cartilage

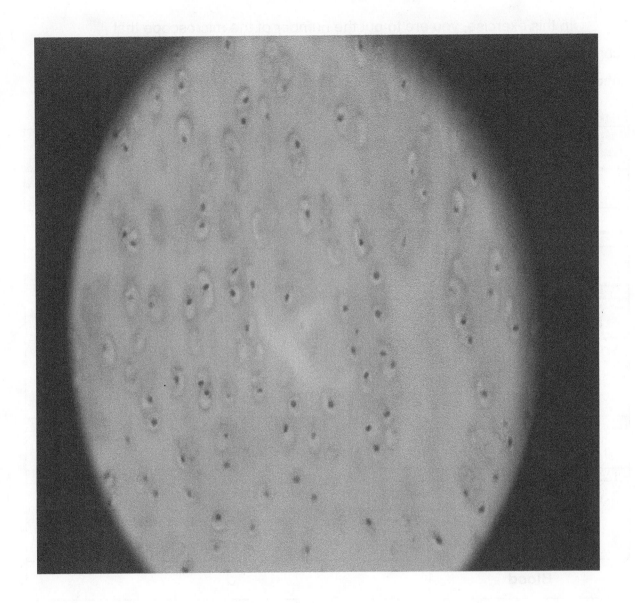

EXERCISE 2-2   CELLS AND TISSUE IDENTIFICATION

(LAB ROOM PICTURES)

In this exercise, you are to put the number of the microscope that corresponds to the cell type in this chart. Then, put the number of the lab room photographs that also correspond to the cell type in this chart.

Cell type	Microscope number	Photograph number
Squamous		
Cuboidal		
Columnar		
Skeletal muscle		
Cardiac muscle		
Smooth muscle		
Neuron / glial cells		
Adipose		
Areolar		
Blood		
Bones		
Cartilage		
Dense		
Reticular		

PRONUNCIATION

1	Areolar (air-ee-oh-lar)	13	Lamina (lam-i-nuh)
2	Basal (bay-sul)	14	Leukocyte (loo-koe-site)
3	Canaliculi (kaa-nuh-li-que-lie)	15	Lumen (loo-mun)
4	Cartilage (kar-ti-lidge)	16	Lymph (lim-ff)
5	Columnar (ku-lum-nar)	17	Neuroglial (ner-oh-glee-ul)
6	Epithelial (eh-pi-thee-lee-ul)	18	Neuron (ner-on)
7	Erythrocyte (eh-ri-throw-site)	19	Osteocyte (os-tee-oh-site)
8	Fibrocytes (fie-broe-sites)	20	Osteon (os-tee-on)
9	Glial (glee-ul)	21	Pseudostratified (soo-doe-straa-ti-fide)
10	Intercalated (in-terk-uh-lay-ted)	22	Soma (so-muh)
11	Lacuna (lah-koo-nuh)	23	Squamous (squay-mus)
12	Lamella (luh-mel-uh)	24	Vacuole (va-que-ohl)

CHAPTER 3   OVERVIEW OF THE REGIONS

The following chapters in this manual are divided in this manner:

Section A: discusses the skeletal structure of a specific region

Section B: discusses the muscles of a specific region

Section C: discusses the blood vessels of a specific region

Section D: discusses the nerves of a specific region

This chapter will discuss general information regarding each of the sections identified above.

CHAPTER 3A: THE STUDY OF BONES

While studying the table below, examine a model of a frontal view of a long bone.

Epiphysis	This is the ends of the long bones.
Diaphysis	This is the shaft of the bone.
Metaphysis	This is the growing point of long bones. It is between the epiphysis and the start of the diaphysis.
Compact bone	This is the parallel edges of long bones.
Spongy bone	This is the bony material that is found in the interior of bones. Most of it is found in the epiphysis.
Trabeculae	These are thin sheets of boney material found in the spongy bone area.
Medullary cavity	This is the cavity within the diaphysis region. It consists of yellow marrow. Yellow marrow produces adipose cells, which are responsible for energy reserves.
Epiphysis cavity	This is the cavity within the epiphysis region. It consists of red marrow. Red marrow produces erythrocytes.

CHAPTER 3B: THE STUDY OF MUSCLES

While studying the table below, examine pictures of muscle fibers. The table below lists the components of a muscle fiber.

Z-disk	Actin myofilaments extend from a protein filament referred to as the Z-disk.
Actin	This is the thin myofilament of muscle cells.
Myosin	This is the thick myofilament of muscle cells.
Sarcomere	A muscle fiber is made of numerous sarcomeres. A sarcomere consists of the region from one Z-disk to another Z-disk. A sarcomere is the functional unit of a muscle.
Sarcolemma	A muscle cell is surrounded by a sarcolemma. A sarcolemma is a cell membrane.
Myofibrils	A muscle cell is made of circular bundles called myofibrils.
Myofilaments	The myofibrils are made of myofilaments that are called actin and myosin.
The arrangement of the actin and myosin create the striped appearance of skeletal muscle cells.	
A muscle cell and a muscle fiber are synonymous terms.	

CHAPTER 3C: THE STUDY OF BLOOD VESSELS

While studying the table below, examine pictures of transverse views of blood vessels. The table below lists the 3 layers of that make up blood vessels.

Tunica interna (intima)	This is inside lining of the blood vessel.
Tunica media	This is the middle layer of the lining of the blood vessel. It is made of smooth muscle, which allows for constriction and dilation of the blood vessel.
Tunica externa (adventitia)	This is the outer layer of the blood vessel. It consists of connective tissue.
Lumen	This is the hollow portion of the vessel making up the tube. Blood flows within the lumen.
The tunica media of an artery is thicker than the tunica media of a vein.	

CHAPTER 3D: THE STUDY OF NERVES

While studying the table below, examine pictures of a neuron. The table below lists the components of a neuron.

Soma	This is the main body of the neuron. It consists of the nucleus and other cell organelles.
Axon	This is the longest part of the neuron. Some axons are microscopic while some are really long, such as the length of the spinal cord or the length of the lower leg (sciatic nerve).
Dendrite	There generally will be several dendrites. These are typically the shorter extension branching off the soma.
The dendrites typically receive the nerve impulse while the axon sends the impulse to a destination.	

CHAPTER 4   THE HEAD AND NECK REGION

Chapter 4 discusses the structures associated with the head and neck region of the body. Chapter 4 is divided into different sections as indicated below:

4A: bones and bone structures of the skull

4B: muscles of the head and neck

4C: blood vessels of the head and in the neck region

4D: nerves of the head (in this case, the brain)

The material used in this lab will be (but not limited to):

Models of the skull

Sagittal head to show muscles

Textbook images of the blood vessels (specifically showing the cerebral arterial circle

Models of the brain

Real sheep brain

Real human brain

Real brains showing meninges

CHAPTER 4A: THE HEAD AND NECK REGION

SKULL BONES AND BONE STRUCTURES

This chapter will discuss the bones of the skull. The skull is part of the axial skeleton. The other parts of the axial skeleton are the associated bones, the thoracic cage, and the vertebral column. The axial division is made of 80 bones.

The skull can be further divided forming the cranial bones and the facial bones. Immovable joints, called *sutures*, join all of the bones of the cranium and face.

The cranium is made of 8 bones. Some of these bones have various processes associated with them, which are not considered to be separate bones. For example, the temporal bone has a structure called the mastoid process. The mastoid process is not a separate bone. The facial region is comprised of 14 bones. Most of the bones occur in pairs except for the mandible and vomer, which are single bones.

There are 7 other bones that are part of the skull but typically are not considered to be part of the cranium or the facial bones. Six of these bones are called the auditory ossicles (malleus, incus, and stapes) and the other bone is the hyoid. The hyoid bone is inferior to the skull suspended by ligaments. It serves as a base for muscle attachments that move the tongue.

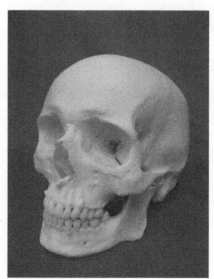

EXERCISE 4A-1   IDENTIFICATION OF BONES AND BONE STRUCTURES

LATERAL SKULL STRUCTURES

At your lab table you have a model of the skull. The information in tables 4A-1 through 4A-11 will help guide you as you identify skull structures. The information uses a beginning landmark and with directional terminology you will be able to find other structures. Use your textbook figures to help you verify the correct structures.

Table 4A-1   Lateral View of the Skull

	Bone or bone structure	Description of the location
1	sagittal suture	Begin with a landmark such as the suture that goes down the middle of the top of the skull
2	parietal bone	Left and right lateral to the sagittal suture
3	temporal bone	Inferior to the parietal bone
4	frontal bone	Anterior to the parietal bones
5	occipital bone	Posterior and a bit inferior to the parietal bones
6	sphenoid	Anterior to the temporal bone (also called the greater wing of the sphenoid)
7	squamosal suture	The suture that connects the parietal bone with the temporal bone
8	lambdoid suture	The suture that connects the occipital bone with the parietal bones
9	mastoid process	A bulge located at the inferior / posterior portion of the temporal bone
10	external auditory meatus	Mostly anterior to the mastoid process
11	styloid process	A bony spine on the inferior skull but yet still a part of the temporal bone

Table 4A-2   Frontal View of the Skull

	Bone or bone structure	Description of the location
1	frontal bone	Making up the forehead
2	maxilla bone	The entire region of the upper jaw
3	Intermaxillary suture	Suture in the anterior center of the maxilla bone
4	Anterior nasal spine	Pointy projection on the maxilla at the superior edge of the intermaxillary suture
5	mandible bone	The entire lower jaw
6	Mandibular condyle on the mandible	A bulge at the center / anterior portion of the mandible
7	mental foramen	Right and left lateral to the mental protuberance are two holes
8	zygomatic bone	The bulges of the cheek bone
9	zygomatic arch	Bony structure that extends from the zygomatic bone to the temporal bone
10	nasal bones	Two bones making up the "bridge" of the nose
11	Frontonasal suture	Suture connecting the nasal bones with the frontal bone
12	Nasomaxillary suture	Suture connecting the nasal bones with the maxillary bone
13	supraorbital foramen	A hole or notch superior to the orbit of the eye socket near the region of the eyebrows
14	infraorbital foramen	A hole inferior to the orbit of the eye socket on the maxilla bone

Table 4A-3   Inside the Nasal Cavity

	Bone or bone structure	Description of the location
1	vomer	The inferior bone of the nasal septum.
2	perpendicular plate of the ethmoid	The superior bony structure of the nasal septum.
3	nasal conchae	Bony bulges on the lateral edge of each nasal cavity. You can see the middle and inferior nasal conchae. You won't be able to see the superior nasal conchae.

Table 4A-4   Inside the Eye Socket

	Bone or bone structure	Description of the location
1	lacrimal bone	The most anterior bone of the medial wall.
2	lacrimal foramen	A hole at the base (distal end) of the lacrimal bone.
3	ethmoid bone	Posterior to the lacrimal bone.
4	sphenoid bone	The posterior wall of the eye socket.
5	optic foramen	The round hole in the sphenoid bone (in the back wall of the eye socket).
6	superior orbital fissure	The superior slit.
7	inferior orbital fissure	The inferior slit.

Table 4A-5 Inferior View of the Skull

	Bone or bone structure	Description of the location
1	foramen magnum	A good landmark to start with is the large hole in the occipital bone
2	basioccipital	Anterior to the foramen magnum is a bony structure that leads toward the posterior nasal openings
3	pharyngeal tubercle	Ridge in the center of the basioccipital.
4	foramen lacerum	The first holes lateral to the basioccipital.
5	foramen ovale	Lateral to the foramen lacerum.
6	foramen spinosum	Just a little posterior and a tad bit lateral to the foramen ovale.
7	carotid foramen (carotid canal)	Posterior to the foramen spinosum.
8	jugular foramen	The large hole posterior to the carotid foramen.
9	occipital condyles	Bulges lateral to the foramen magnum.
10	condyloid foramen	Small holes posterior to the occipital condyles.
11	hypoglossal canal	Holes that appear to go "under" the occipital condyles.

Table 4A-6   Inferior View of the Skull   (Roof of the Mouth)

	Bone or bone structure	Description of the location
1	anterior palatine	Anterior 2/3 of the roof of the mouth. Also called the palatine process of the maxilla.
2	posterior palatine	Posterior 1/3 of the roof of the mouth. Also called the palatine bone.
3	Incisive foramen	Hole in the anterior palatine bone immediately posterior to the incisor teeth. The foramen is located in the center of the incisive fossa.
4	greater palatine foramen	Holes at the lateral edge of the posterior palatine bone.
5	median palatine suture	Sagittal suture of the anterior palatine.
6	palatomaxillary suture	Transverse suture connecting the anterior palatine with the posterior palatine.
7	choana	Posterior nasal openings "under" the posterior palatine bone.

Table 4A-7   Internal View of the Skull

1	foramen magnum	A good landmark to begin with is the large hole in the skull (foramen in the occipital bone).
2	clivus	Extending anterior (at a slant) from the foramen magnum is a bony structure that leads to a ridge (the dorsum sella).
3	dorsum sella	The bony ridge at the end of the clivus
4	hypophyseal fossa	A deep depression anterior to the dorsum sella.
5	tuberculum sella	Anterior to the hypophyseal fossa is another ridge.
6	sella turcica	The collective term for the dorsum sella, hypophyseal fossa, and tuberculum sella. This term means, "like a Turkish saddle."
7	sphenoid	The sella turcica is a structure that is a part of the sphenoid bone. Follow the sphenoid bone laterally to the greater wing of the sphenoid.
8	hypophysis (pituitary gland)	This structure from our brain sits in the hypophyseal fossa for protection.
9	optic foramen (canal)	On either side of the tuberculum sella is a hole that the optic nerve from the eye passes through in order to transmit impulses to the brain for interpretation of vision.
10	crista galli	The pointy ridge at the anterior portion of the skull
11	cribriform plate	The plate, with holes, that outlines the crista galli.

12	foramen lacerum	Right and left lateral to the dorsum sella are two holes
13	foramen ovale	A hole lateral to the foramen lacerum (and perhaps a smidget anterior)
14	foramen rotundum	A hole anterior to the foramen ovale.
15	foramen spinosum	A hole a little posterior and a tad bit lateral to the foramen ovale.
16	carotid canal (carotid foramen)	A hole medial and posterior to the foramen spinosum.
17	petrous portion of the temporal bone	A ridge that angles oblique and posterior to the carotid canal.
18	jugular foramen	On the posterior side of that ridge you will find two holes. One is superior and smaller; the other is inferior and larger. The inferior one is the jugular foramen.
19	internal acoustic meatus	The hole superior to the jugular foramen.
20	cribriform plate foramina	The numerous holes in the cribriform plate. Also called olfactory foramina.

Table 4A-8   Internal View of the Skull

There are four major bones making up the internal view of the skull. The curved shape of these bones creates three cranial fossa. Use your textbook to help you identify the following bones:

1	**occipital**	This bone consists of the foramen magnum. The depressed area is the posterior cranial fossa.
2	**sphenoid**	This bone consists of the sella turcica.
3	**temporal**	There are two temporal bones. Each one lies between the occipital bone and the sphenoid bone. The depressed area is the middle cranial fossa.
4	**frontal**	This bone is anterior to the sphenoid. The depressed area is the anterior cranial fossa.

The occipital lobe of the brain sits in the posterior cranial fossa.

The temporal lobe of the brain sits in the middle cranial fossa.

The frontal lobe of the brain sits in the anterior cranial fossa.

Table 4A-9   The Mandible

1	**mandibular condyle**	The hinge joint of the mandible is made of two bony structures. This one is the rounded portion of the joint. Some books called it the "head of the mandible."
2	**mandibular fossa**	The other portion of the jaw joint is a depression in the zygomatic process of the temporal bone.
3	**mandibular notch**	Anterior to the mandibular condyle is a curved area.
4	**coronoid process**	Anterior to the mandibular notch is a pointy projection.
5	**ramus**	Inferior to the mandibular notch, all the way down to the angle of the mandible.
6	**angle of the mandible**	The posterior edge of the mandible that feels like a bulge near the earlobe.
7	**body**	The majority of the mandible.
8	**mental protuberance**	A bony ridge in the middle of the anterior portion of the mandible. This is in the "dimple" area of the chin.
9	**mental foramen**	Lateral to the mental protuberance are two holes.
10	**alveolar processes**	The bony bulges near the teeth (tooth sockets).

Table 4A-10   The Teeth

1	alveolar processes	The teeth sit in sockets that form small bumps on the maxillary bone and mandible bone.
2	incisors	The four front teeth. 4 per jaw.
3	cuspids	Lateral to the incisors. 2 per jaw.
4	bicuspids	The next two teeth that are mostly posterior to the cuspids. 4 per jaw.
5	molars	The next three teeth that are mostly posterior to the bicuspids. Up to 6 per jaw.
6	wisdom teeth	These are the most posterior molars. Not everyone has the last set of molars.

Table 4A-11   Additional Skull Structures

1	calvaria	This is a collective term for the skullcap. The skullcap is made of the parietal, frontal, and occipital bones.
2	auditory ossicles	The auditory ossicles are the 3 smallest bones of the body. They are called the malleus, incus, and stapes. These are located in the middle ear just outside the petrous portion of the temporal bone.
3	anterior fontanel	This is the baby's anterior "soft spot."
4	posterior fontanel	This is the baby's posterior "soft spot."

EXERCISE 4A-2 PALPATING BONES AND BONE STRUCTURES

PALPATING SKULL STRUCTURES

Now that you have studied a few of the structures, palpate the following structures on your own body and have a partner verify that you are palpating the correct structure.

1. Zygomatic bone
2. Zygomatic arch
3. Mandibular angle
4. Mental protuberance
5. Alveolar processes on the maxilla
6. Mandibular condyle on the skull in the TMJ area
7. Mastoid process
8. Alveolar processes

PRONUNCIATION

1	Acoustic (uh-koo-stik)		16	Fontanel (fon-tuh-nel)
2	Alveolar (al-vee-oh-lar)		17	Foramen (for-ay-men)
3	Basioccipital (bay-see-ok-si-pi-tul)		18	Foramina (for-aa-mi-nuh)
4	Calvaria (kal-vare-ee-uh)		19	Frontonasal (fron-toe-nay-sul)
5	Carotid (ku-raw-tid)		20	Hypoglossal (high-poe-glos-sul)
6	Choana (koe-ay-nuh)		21	Hypophyseal (high-pof-i-see-ul)
7	Clivus (kly-vus)		22	Hypophysis (high-pof-i-sis)
8	Conchae (kong-kay) Concha (kong-kuh)		23	Incisive (in-sigh-siv)
9	Condyle (kon-dile)		24	Incisors (in-sigh-zors)
10	Condyloid (kon-di-loyd)		25	Infraorbital (in-fruh-or-bi-tul)
11	Coronoid (kor-uh-noyd)		26	Jugular (jug-you-lar)
12	Cribriform (kri-bri-form)		27	Lacerum (laa-sir-um)
13	Crista galli (kris-tuh gal-ee)		28	Lacrimal (laa-kri-mul)
14	Cuspids (kus-pids)		29	Lambdoid (lam-doyd)
15	Ethmoid (eth-moyd)		30	Mandible (man-di-bull)

31	Maxilla (mak-sil-uh)	45	Rotundum (roe-ton-dum)
32	Meatus (mee-ay-tus)	46	Sagittal (saa-ji-tul)
33	Molars (moe-lars)	47	Sella (sell-uh)
34	Nasal (nay-sul)	48	Sphenoid (sfeh-noyd) (sfee-noyd)
35	Occipital (ok-si-pi-tul)	49	Spinosum (spy-no-sum)
36	Ossicles (os-si-kuls)	50	Squamosal (squaw-moe-sul)
37	Ovale (oh-vay-lee)	51	Styloid (stie-loyd)
38	Palatine (pal-uh-tyne)	52	Supraorbital (soo-pruh-or-bi-tul)
39	Palatomaxillary (pal-uh-toe-mak-si-larry)	53	Temporal (tem-poor-ul)
40	Parietal (puh-rye-eh-tul)	54	Tuberculum sellae (too-ber-kew-lum sell-ee)
41	Petrous (peh-trus)	55	Turcica (ter-si-kuh)
42	Pharyngeal tubercle (fair-in-jee-ul too ber-kul)	56	Vomer (voe-mer)
43	Protuberance (proe-too-ber-unce)	57	Zygomatic (zie-go-maa-tik)
44	Ramus (ray-mus)		

CHAPTER 4B   THE HEAD AND NECK REGION

SKELETAL MUSCLES

This lab session involves the identification of the skeletal muscles of the head and neck. Most of the muscles of the head are involved in facial expressions and most of the muscles in the neck (anterior neck) are involved with mastication or swallowing. Some of the muscles insert and attach to a bone or bony projection while others insert and attach to fascia tissue.

Other muscles of the face include the extraocular muscles of the eye. These muscles move the eyeball and will be studied in a later chapter.

There are over 75 different muscles comprising the head and neck. Of these 75, we will concentrate on 25 to 30 muscles.

In this lab, you will view a sagittal head that shows most of the muscles we will study. There are some muscles not found on the model so you will need to rely on textbook pictures.

So, how many muscles does it take to smile? Who knows? What does your smile look like?

EXERCISE 4B-1   IDENTIFICATION OF SKELETAL MUSCLES OF THE HEAD

Table 4B-1   Face and Neck Muscles

	POSITION DESCRIPTION	MUSCLE
1	The muscle that covers the frontal bone is the frontalis.	**Frontalis**
2	The muscle that encircles the eye is the orbicularis oculi.	**Orbicularis oculi**
3	The muscle that encircles the mouth is the orbicularis oris.	**Orbicularis oris**
Orbicularis is in reference to a circular muscle. Oculi is in reference to the eye and oris is in reference to the mouth.		
4	The muscle covering the nasal bone is the nasalis.	**Nasalis**
5	Find the muscle that extends from the orbicularis oculi region to the upper lip.	**Levator labii superioris**
6	This muscle extends from the orbicularis oris, passes near the ala of the nose and inserts near the medial corner of the eye socket.	**Levator labii superioris alaeque nasi**
Extending from the corner of the lip to the zygomatic bone are two muscles called the zygomaticus muscles.		
7	The superior zygomatic muscle is the zygomaticus minor.	**Zygomaticus minor**
8	The inferior zygomatic muscle is the zygomaticus major.	**Zygomaticus major**
9	Extending from the corner of the lip toward the earlobe is the risorius.	**Risorius**
The risorius originates in the fascia covering the masseter muscle.		
10	The most lateral muscle of the face is a large jaw muscle called the masseter.	**Masseter**

Table 4B-1   Face and Neck Muscles (continued)

	POSITION DESCRIPTION	MUSCLE
11	The muscle that is deep to the masseter, thus occupying the space between the lateral border of the body of the mandible and the maxilla is the buccinator muscle.	**Buccinator**
12	Extending from the lower lip to the middle of the anterior mandible is the mentalis muscle.	**Mentalis**
13	Lateral to the mentalis is the depressor labii inferioris.	**Depressor labii inferioris**
14	Lateral to the depressor labii inferioris is the depressor anguli oris.	**Depressor anguli oris**
15	Making up the floor of the mandible is the mylohyoid muscle.	**Mylohyoid**
16	On the surface of the mylohyoid are two "bulging muscles" called the digastrics.	**Digastric**
17	Covering the entire anterior neck is the platysma.	**Platysma**
The platysma has been removed in pictures and on the models so you can see the deeper muscles of the neck region.		
Find the muscle that extends from the mastoid process to the sternum and clavicle.		
This muscle divides so part of it attaches to the manubrium and another part attaches to the clavicle.		
18	This muscle is the sternocleidomastoid	**Sternocleidomastoid**
"Sterno" because it attaches to a part of the sternum. "Cleido" because part of it attaches to the clavicle. "Mastoid" because part of it attaches to the mastoid process.		

Table 4B-1   Face and Neck Muscles (continued)

	POSITION DESCRIPTION	MUSCLE
19	Look at the anterior view of the neck. You will see a fairly vertical muscle. This muscle extends from the sternum to the hyoid bone.	**Sternohyoid**
20	Posterior to the sternohyoid there is a muscle that angles toward the scapula.	**Omohyoid**
21	Between the sternohyoid and omohyoid (deep to the sternohyoid) is the sternothyroid.	**Sternothyroid**
22	Locate the trapezius muscle (upper back muscle. This muscle extends to the occipital region of the skull.	**Trapezius**

There are several muscles between the trapezius and the sternocleidomastoid.

Put your finger on the distal end of the clavicular portion of the sternocleidomastoid.

23	Move your finger posterior. Your finger should be on the anterior scalene muscle	**Anterior scalene**
24	Move posterior again and you will find the middle scalene.	**Middle scalene**
25	Move posterior and deep, you will find the posterior scalene.	**Posterior scalene**
26	Move posterior again and you will find the levator scapulae.	**Levator scapulae**
27	Posterior again and you will find the splenius muscle.	**Splenius**
28	The muscle on the posterior aspect of the head is the occipitalis.	**Occipitalis**
29	The muscle in the frons area is the frontalis.	**Frontalis**
30	The muscle in the temporal region is the temporalis.	**Temporalis**

PRONUNCIATION

1	Buccinator (buk-si-nay-tor)	12	Orbicularis oculi (or-bik-you-lar-is ok-you-lie)
2	Capitis (kaa-pi-tis)	13	Orbicularis oris (or-bik-you-lar-is or-is)
3	Depressor anguli oris (dee-press-or ang-you-lie)	14	Platysma (pluh-tees-muh)
4	Digastric (die-gas-trik)	15	Quadratus (kwah-dray-tus)
5	Frontalis (frun-tal-is)	16	Risorius (rye-zor-ee-us)
6	Levator labii superioris (leh-vay-tor lay-bee—eye soo-peer-ee-or-is)	17	Scalene (skay-leen)
7	Masseter (muh-see-ter)	18	Sternocleidomastoid (stern-oh-cly-doe-mas-toyd)
8	Mentalis (men-tal-is)	19	Sternohyoid (stern-oh-high-oyd)
9	Mylohyoid (my-low-high-oyd)	20	Sternothyroid (stern-oh-thigh-oyd)
10	Nasalis (nay-za-lis)	21	Tensor fasciae latae (ten-sor fay-she-ee lay-tuh)
11	Omohyoid (oh-mo-high-oyd)	22	Zygomaticus (zie-go-maa-ti-kus)

CHAPTER 4C   THE HEAD AND NECK REGION

BLOOD VESSELS

This lab session involves the study of the blood vessels that supply the head and the brain. The blood vessels going to the head and brain arise either directly or indirectly from the aortic arch. The blood vessels we will study supply the superficial aspect of the face and cranium and also to the pituitary gland. You will find that the pituitary gland has a very unique set of vessels that circle around the gland, called the cerebral arterial circle.

The majority of the supply to the head region is via the external carotid artery and internal carotid artery. The external carotid artery branches to form superficial arteries and the internal carotid artery eventually supplies the pituitary gland.

Cool stuff:

Place your finger on the temporal bone area and you will feel pulsating in the temporal artery.

Place your finger in the middle of the body of the mandible. You will feel pulsating in the facial artery.

EXERCISE 4C-1   IDENTIFICATION OF BLOOD VESSELS

The best way to study the blood vessels is to look at a model or a diagram and put your finger on one blood vessel and trace the flow of blood with your finger. For example, put your finger on the aortic arch, which is an aorta that emerges from the heart. Then, follow the list of blood vessels below.

Table 4C-1   Blood Vessels (arteries)

Aortic arch	Aortic arch	Aortic arch	Aortic arch
Brachiocephalic artery	Brachiocephalic artery	Brachiocephalic artery	Brachiocephalic artery
R. Common carotid a	R. Common carotid a	R. Common carotid a	R. Common carotid a
R. External carotid a	R. External carotid a	R. External carotid a	R. Internal carotid a
Facial a	Occipital a	Superficial temporal a	Cerebral arterial circle

Aortic arch	Aortic arch
R. subclavian a	L. subclavian a
Vertebral a	Vertebral a
Basilar a	Basilar a
Cerebral arterial circle	Cerebral arterial circle

Aortic arch	Aortic arch	Aortic arch	Aortic arch
L. Common carotid a	L. Common carotid a	L. Common carotid a	L. Common carotid a
L. External carotid a	L. External carotid a	L. External carotid a	L. Internal carotid a
Facial a	Occipital a	Superficial temporal a	Cerebral arterial circle

Table 4C-2   Blood Vessels (veins)

Vein sinuses	Facial v	Vein sinuses	Facial v
Internal jugular v	Internal jugular v	Internal jugular v	Internal jugular v
R. brachiocephalic v	R. brachiocephalic v	L. brachiocephalic v	L. brachiocephalic v
Superior vena cava	Superior vena cava	Superior vena cava	Superior vena cava
Right atrium of the heart			

Temporal v	Occipital v	Temporal v	Occipital v
External jugular v	External jugular v	External jugular v	External jugular v
R. brachiocephalic v	R. brachiocephalic v	L. brachiocephalic v	L. brachiocephalic v
Superior vena cava	Superior vena cava	Superior vena cava	Superior vena cava
Right atrium of the heart			

Vein sinuses	Vein sinuses
Vertebral v	Vertebral v
R. brachiocephalic v	L. brachiocephalic v
Superior vena cava	Superior vena cava
Right atrium of the heart	

CHAPTER 4D   THE HEAD AND NECK REGION

THE BRAIN

The nervous system of the body can be divided into the *central nervous system* and the *peripheral nervous system.* The central nervous system is made of the brain and the spinal cord. The peripheral nervous system makes up the nerves going to and from the central nervous system. This chapter deals with the central nervous system, primarily the brain. The spinal cord will be discussed in a later chapter.

The brain contains about 35 billion neurons. It contains almost 98% of all the neurons of the body and has a mass of 1.5 Kg. The brain is a very complex organ. Most people are familiar with the brain with reference to thought processes and emotions. After studying this chapter, you will find out just how complex the brain really is.

In order to begin to understand the brain's complexity, anatomists have tried to simplify the study of the brain by organizing the brain into various divisions and subdivisions. The brain is first divided into 5 main regions or landmarks. These regions are the *telencephalon, diencephalon, mesencephalon, metencephalon,* and *myelencephalon.* These regions have been subdivided into various structures. The central nervous system is protected by a group of three membranes called *the meninges* and skeletal structures, the skull and vertebrae.

At your lab table, you have a model of a human brain and a dissected sheep brain. Read the information that is in tables 4D-1 through 4D-3. The information in those tables will help guide you through the structures of the external and internal view of the brain. Identify those parts on the brain model and in your textbook. Then, find those same parts on the real brains in the lab room.

EXERCISE 4D-1   THE EXTERNAL AND INTERNAL BRAIN STRUCTURES

Table 4D-1   External Brain Structures

1	**Cerebrum**	The entire outer portion of the brain that consists of valleys and ridges.
2	**Cerebellum**	The cerebellum is the mass of tissue mostly inferior to the posterior portion of the cerebrum.
3	**Longitudinal fissure**	If you look at the superior portion of the cerebrum you will see that it consist of a left hemisphere and a right hemisphere. There is a deep fissure between the two hemispheres the runs the length of the cerebrum.
4	**Gyri**	The ridges found on the cerebrum. Singular is gyrus.
5	**Sulci**	The valleys between the ridges. Singular is sulcus.
6	**Lobes**	The cerebrum consists of 4 lobes that can be seen from an external view.

Occipital lobe
This is the posterior portion of the brain mostly superior to the cerebellum.

Frontal lobe
This is the most anterior portion of the brain.

Parietal lobe
This is the area between the frontal lobe and the occipital lobe.

Temporal lobe
This is a bulgy lobe located on the lateral sides of the brain. You will see a deep fissure separating the temporal lobe from the rest of the cerebrum.

7	**Lateral cerebral fissure**	This is the deep fissure between the temporal lobe and the rest of the cerebrum.

Table 4D-2   Sagittal Brain Structures

1	corpus callosum	Put your finger on the corpus callosum.
2	cerebrum	The entire area superior to the corpus callosum is the cerebrum.

The cerebrum consists of five lobes **frontal, parietal, temporal, occipital, limbic** (some refer to the limbic as a "lobe")

3	cingulate gyrus	Immediately superior to the corpus callosum is a gyrus, which is part of the cerebrum. The cingulate gyrus is one part of the limbic lobe.
4	fornix	Appearing to angle inferior to the corpus callosum is a bundle of nerves called the fornix.
5	choroid plexus	Located lining the inferior edge of the fornix is the choroid plexus.
6	thalamus	Anterior to the fornix area is the lateral ventricle. Posterior to the fornix area is the thalamus area. There is a right and left ventricle (ventricle 1 and ventricle 2). A membrane separates the two ventricles. It is called the septum pallucidum.
7	hypothalamus	Angling inferior and slightly anterior to the thalamus is the hypothalamus.
8	pituitary gland	Attached to the hypothalamus is the pituitary gland (anatomically called the hypophysis).
9	Infundibulum	This is a stalk that connects the pituitary to the hypothalamus.
10	mammillary body	Put your finger in the center of the hypothalamus. Move to the posterior wall of the hypothalamus. There is a bulge called the mammillary body.

Table 4D-2   Sagittal Brain Structures   (continued)

1	**pons**	Put your finger in the center of the thalamus area. Move inferior as though you are going down the spinal cord region. You will find a rather large bulge.
2	**medulla oblongata**	Inferior to the pons you will find a smaller bulge.
3	**spinal cord**	Extending from the medulla oblongata is the spinal cord.
4	**midbrain**	Put one finger in the center of the thalamus and another finger on the pons. The area between the pons and the thalamus is the midbrain.
5	**corpora quadrigemina**	The posterior portion of the midbrain is the corpora quadrigemina. It consists of two bumps: one is the superior colliculus and the other is the inferior colliculus.
6	**cerebellum**	Posterior to the pons and inferior to the occipital lobe of the cerebrum is a cauliflower-looking structure called the cerebellum.

ok at the inferior view of the sheet brain your instructor has on display. Observe the cranial
rves your instructor has identified. List those nerves in table 4D-3 below. Also, observe the sheep
ain that shows the meninges.

Table 4D-3   Sheep Brains on Display

Observe the following cranial nerves	Observe the meninges
	Dura mater
	Arachnoid
	Pia mater

Table 4D-4   Sagittal Brain Structures   (Ventricles of the brain)

1	Lateral ventricle	There is a cavity between the fornix and the corpus callosum. There is one cavity within one hemisphere and another cavity in the other hemisphere. Therefore, the two lateral ventricles are called ventricle 1 and ventricle 2.
2	Septum pallucidum	This is the membranous partition between the two lateral ventricles.
3	Third ventricle	This ventricle is the depressed area within the thalamus region.
4	Fourth ventricle	This is the cavity between the pons and the cerebellum.
5	Choroid plexus	You will find the choroid plexus located in a portion of the third ventricle along the inferior edges of the corpus callosum area and the superior edge of the fornix. Choroid plexus is also found in the fourth ventricle.

Cerebrospinal fluid is produced by the choroid plexus, enters the lateral ventricles, flows through the interventricular foramen, into the third ventricle, through the aqueduct of the midbrain, into the fourth ventricle, then around the spinal cord and cerebrum.

EXERCISE 4D-2   BRAIN FUNCTIONS

To help you learn the anatomical structures of the brain, it is helpful to have an understanding of the functions of the individual structures. Table 4D-4 has a partial list of functions. Keep in mind, many structures of the brain have multiple functions and many structures have overlapping functions. However, table 4D-4 limits the brain structures to one or two functions for simplicity.

Table 4D-4   Brain Structure Functions

1	**Cerebrum**	Thought processes, mathematical ability, language, and speech.
2	**Cerebellum**	Coordinates smooth motor activities from the cerebrum.
3	**Thalamus**	Acts as a relay station to and from the cerebrum. Contains a portion of the RAS. The reticular activating system is the body's alert system.
4	**Hypothalamus**	Produces some hormones, controls thirst and some emotions.
5	**Hypophysis**	Produces and secretes numerous hormones.
6	**Pons**	Regulates breathing and heart rate by increasing or decreasing the rates.
7	**Medulla oblongata**	Regulates breathing and heart rate by maintaining rhythmic rates. Involved in involuntary reflexes such as vomiting, sneezing, and coughing.
8	**Corpus callosum**	A bundle of nerves connecting the left hemisphere with the right hemisphere.
9	**Frontal lobe**	Primary motor controls
10	**Parietal lobe**	Interprets sensory information from taste buds and visceral organs and interprets touch sensations.

Table 4D-4   Brain Structure Functions   (continued)

11	**Occipital lobe**	Interprets vision
12	**Temporal lobe**	Interprets odors and hearing
13	**Limbic lobe (system)**	Contains areas relating to long-term memory
14	**Left hemisphere**	Major speech centers, writing skills, and mathematical skills.
15	**Right hemisphere**	Major analysis of touch and spatial relationships.
16	**Choroid plexus**	Produces cerebrospinal fluid.
17	**Corpora quadrigemina**	Consists of superior colliculi and inferior colliculi. The superior colliculi are involved in visual orientation. The inferior colliculi are involved in auditory orientation. Superior colliculi – we see something in our peripheral vision, we turn our head in that direction. Inferior colliculi – we hear something, we turn our head in that direction.

PRONUNCIATION

#	Term	#	Term
1	Arachnoid (uh-rak-noyd)	10	Fornix (for-niks)
2	Cerebellum (ser-uh-bel-lum)	11	Gyri (jie-rye)
3	Cerebrum (sir-ree-brum)	12	Hypophysis (high-pof-i-sis)
4	Choroid plexus (kor-royd pleks-us)	13	Hypothalamus (high-po-thal-u-mus)
5	Cingulate (sin-gyou-late)	14	Infundibulum (in-fun-dib-you-lum)
6	Colliculi (koe-lick-you-ly)	15	Pia mater (pee-uh may-ter)
7	Corpora quadrigemina (kor-por-uh kwa-dri-jeh-meh-nuh)	16	Septum pallucidum (sep-tum puh-loo-si-dum)
8	Corpus callosum (kor-pus kuh-low-sum)	17	Sulci (sul-ki)
9	Dura mater (der-uh may-ter)	18	Thalamus (thal-uh-mus)

CHAPTER 5   THE UPPER APPENDAGE

Chapter 5 discusses the structures associated with the upper appendage, which include the shoulder, upper arm, lower arm, and the wrist and hand. Chapter 5 is divided into different sections as indicated below:

> 5A: bones and bone structures of the upper appendage
>
> 5B: muscles of the upper appendage
>
> 5C: blood vessels of the upper appendage
>
> 5D: nerves of the upper appendage (cervical and brachial plexus)
>
> 5E: shoulder joint and elbow joint

The material used in this lab will be (but not limited to):

Models of the upper skeleton (disarticulated)

Fully articulated skeleton

Arm muscle models

Arm blood vessel models

Textbook images of the brachial plexus

Models of the shoulder and elbow joint

CHAPTER 5A THE UPPER APPENDICULAR REGION

THE APPENDICULAR SKELETON (PECTORAL GIRDLE AND ITS APPENDAGE)

The appendicular skeleton consists of 126 bones and can be divided into two major categories, the *pectoral girdle* and its appendages and the *pelvic girdle* and its appendages. This chapter deals with the pectoral girdle and its appendages. The pectoral girdle is made of the scapula and clavicle bones.

In this class we will study in detail the various landmarks associated with the shoulder, arm, and hand bones. We do not study these landmarks for the sake of something to memorize. Each of these landmarks has special significance. In many cases, the landmarks are places for muscles to attach.

Students entering into a radiology program of study will find that this information will become a part of their life on the job. Students entering into a nursing program will also find that having knowledge of bone structures will also become a part of their life on the job. Many bone landmarks become a point of reference for the nurse when taking measurements or when finding the proper place to "stick a needle in the patient."

At any rate, in this class we study more than:

♪ The arm bones are connected to the shoulder bones. ♫

EXERCISE 5A-1 IDENTIFICATION OF SKELETAL BONES AND BONE STRUCTURES

At your lab table you have a box of a complete disarticulated skeleton. The information in tables 5A-1 through 5A-8 will help guide you as you identify skeletal structures. Use your textbook figures to help you verify the structures. Be sure to examine the skeleton that is hanging in the middle of lab room.

Table 5A-1   The Clavicle

1	**acromial end**	One end of the clavicle is narrower than the other end. The narrower end is the acromial end.
2	**sternal end**	One end of the clavicle appears to be "squared off."
3	**conoid tubercle**	On the inferior side and nearest the acromial end is a bulge.

Table 5A-2   The Scapula

1	spinous process	Put your finger on the spinous process, which is a posterior ridge of the scapula.
2	acromion	Move your finger to the lateral edge of the spinous process. You will encounter a bulge called the acromion.
3	coracoid process	The bulge immediately anterior to the acromion is the coracoid process.
4	supraspinous fossa	The depression immediately superior to the spinous process.
5	infraspinous fossa	Inferior to the spinous process is a depression called the infraspinous fossa.
6	lateral border	Put your finger on the lateral border.
7	inferior angle	Move your finger all the way down the lateral border to the inferior rounded portion of the scapula.
8	glenoid fossa (cavity)	Move our finger along the lateral border all the way to the superior depression of the scapula.
9	medial border	The medial border is the longer border on the opposite edge of the scapula.
10	superior angle	Run your finger along the medial border to the "top" of the scapula. You will find a rounded edge called the superior angle.
11	scapular notch (suprascapular notch)	There is a notch between the superior angle and the coracoid process, nearest the coracoid process.
12	body	The main portion of the scapula is the body.
13	subscapular fossa	On the anterior side of the body near the superior angle and the scapular notch is a shallow depression

Table 5A-3   The Humerus

1	**head**	Put your finger on the superior, rounded, medial bulge of the humerus. The head fits in the glenoid fossa of the scapula.
2	**greater tubercle**	Move your finger laterally to find a bulge on the lateral side of the humerus at the proximal end.
3	**lesser tubercle**	Move your finger around to the anterior edge at the proximal end to find a smaller bulge.
4	**capitulum**	At the distal end, on the anterior side, you will see two rounded bulges. One appears to be rounded and the other appears to be "chopped off." The rounded, lateral bulge is the capitulum.
5	**trochlea**	From the rounded capitulum, move medially to find the trochlea, which appears to "squared off."
6	**coronoid fossa**	Move your finger to the middle of the distal end of the humerus. Then, move your finger superior to a depression.
7	**olecranon fossa**	On the posterior side, opposite the coronoid fossa, is a larger fossa.
8	**medial epicondyle**	At the distal end on the medial side (medial to the trochlea) is a rather large bulge.
9	**lateral epicondyle**	At the distal end on the lateral side (lateral to the capitulum) is a smaller bulge.
10	**deltoid tuberosity**	If you run your fingers along the shaft of the bone nearest the greater tubercle on the lateral edge, you will notice a rough area to the touch. This rough area is for muscle attachment.

Table 5A-4   The Radius

1	head	The proximal portion of the radius consists of a round structure with a depression in it. The head pivots on the capitulum of the humerus.
	radial tuberosity	Inferior to the head is a bulge that forms mostly on the medial side of the radius.
2	**styloid process**	At the distal end there is a pointy projection sort-of to the lateral edge.
3	**dorsal radial tuberosity**	Medial to the styloid process (and on the posterior side) is a series of bumps.
Opposite the dorsal radial tuberosity is the anterior portion of the radius. This region is quite smooth.		

Table 5A-5   The Ulna

1	**trochlear notch**	On the anterior side, there is a major curved portion at the proximal end (looks like an ice cream scoop).
2	**olecranon (process)**	The posterior bulge (proximal end). This is the elbow.
3	**coronoid process**	If you run your finger in the trochlear notch you will find an anterior "lip" at the lower end of the trochlear notch.
4	**radial notch of the ulna**	Lateral to the trochlear notch is a very shallow depression.
5	**styloid process**	At the distal end, there is a small pointy projection.

Table 5A-6   The Carpals

1	**capitate**	A good starting point would be the carpal that is in the middle. It is rather elongated.
2	**hamate**	Medial to the capitate is the carpal with the hook.
3	**pisiform**	Medial to the hamate are two carpals. One carpal is sitting on the other. The rounded one that appears to be sitting "on top" (it's really sitting anterior) is the pisiform.
4	**triquetrum**	The pisiform is sitting on the triquetrum.
5	**lunate**	Lateral to the triquetrum
6	**scaphoid**	Lateral to the lunate
7	**trapezium**	Distal to the scaphoid. The trapezium is in "line" with the thumb.
8	**trapezoid**	Medial to the trapezium and sitting between the trapezium and the capitate is a small bone that appears to be "trapped" between two larger bones.

Table 5A-7   The Metacarpals

1	**metacarpal number 1**	The most lateral metacarpal (in line with the thumb).
2	**metacarpal number 2**	The metacarpal in line with our first finger.
3	**metacarpal number 3**	The metacarpal in line with our middle finger.
4	**metacarpal number 4**	The metacarpal in line with our ring finger.
5	**metacarpal number 5**	The metacarpal in line with the little finger.

Table 5A-8   The Phalanges

1	**proximal and distal phalanges**	The pollex has two phalanges.
2	**proximal, middle, and distal phalanges**	All other digits have three phalanges.
	The thumb is counted as digit number 1.	

Exercise 5A-2 Palpation of Bony Structures

The following is a partial list of bone structures that you can feel on your body. You should be able to palpate these structures and others after studying bone identification.

Greater tubercle

Olecranon process

Medial and lateral epicondyle

Styloid process of the ulna

Table 5A-9   Examination of the Skeleton

1. Observe the positioning of the clavicle.

2. Observe how the coracoid process and acromion serve to partially protect the ball and socket joint of the arm.

3. Examine how the coronoid process of the ulna fits into the coronoid fossa of the humerus when the lower arm is flexed.

4. Examine how the olecranon of the ulna fits into the olecranon fossa of the humerus when the lower arm is extended.

5. Examine which carpal/s actually hinge with the radius.

6. Examine which carpal/s actually hinge with the ulna.

PRONUNCIATION

1	Acromial (uh-krow-mee-ul)		13	Phalanges (fuh-lan-jees)
2	Capitate (ka-pi-tate)		14	Pisiform (pie-zi-form)
3	Capitulum (kuh-pitch-you-lum)		15	Scaphoid (skaa-foid)
4	Conoid (koe-noyd)		16	Scapular (skap-you-lar)
5	Coracoid (kor-uh-coyd)		17	Styloid (stie-loyd)
6	Coronoid (kor-uh-noyd)		18	Trapezium (truh-pee-zee-um)
7	Epicondyle (eh-pi-kon-dile)		19	Trapezoid (traa-peh-zoyd)
8	Glenoid (glee-noid)		20	Triquetrum (try-kwee-trum)
9	Hamate (haa-mate)		21	Trochlea (trok-lee -uh)
10	Lunate (loo-nate)		22	Trochlear (trok-lee -ar)
11	Metacarpal (meh-tuh-kar-pul)		23	Tubercle (too-ber-kul)
12	Olecranon (oh-lek-ruh-non)		24	Tuberosity (too-ber-oss-i-tee)

CHAPTER 5B   THE UPPER APPENDICULAR REGION

SKELETAL MUSCLES

While studying the muscles, you will find that many have names that are similar to the name of the bone they are on.

In this class we study not only the names of muscles but the origin, insertion, and action of the muscles. These topics will be studied in lecture rather than in the laboratory setting.

We will study at least 60 muscles of the upper appendage

Exercise 5B-1 Identification of Skeletal Muscles

Table 5B-1   Upper Arm Muscles

	POSITION DESCRIPTION	MUSCLE
1	Find the biceps brachii muscle on the anterior upper arm.	**Biceps brachii**
	There are two parts to the biceps brachii.	
2	The lateral part is the long head of the biceps brachii.	**Long head**
3	The medial part is the short head of the biceps brachii.	**Short head**
4	Put your finger on the muscle near the proximal portion of the short head. Move medial and our finger will be on the coracobrachialis.	**Coracobrachialis**
5	Deep to the biceps brachii is the brachialis.	**Brachialis**
6	Find the triceps brachii.	**Triceps brachii**
	There are three parts to the triceps brachii	
7	The most medial part is the long head of the triceps brachii.	**Long head**
8	The most lateral part is the lateral head of the triceps brachii.	**Lateral head**
9	Deep to the long head and lateral head is the medial head of the triceps brachii.	**Medial head**

Table 5B-2   Lower Arm Muscles

	POSITION DESCRIPTION	MUSCLE
1	Find the palmaris longus muscle on the anterior lower arm.	**Palmaris longus**
	Put your finger in the middle of the palmaris longus.	
2	Move medial and your finger will be on the flexor carpi ulnaris.	**Flexor carpi ulnaris**
	Go back to the palmaris longus.	
3	Move your finger lateral. You will be on the flexor carpi radialis.	**Flexor carpi radialis**
4	Move lateral one more time and your finger will be on a huge lateral muscle called the brachioradialis.	**Brachioradialis**
	Go back to the palmaris longus.	
	Move your finger to the distal end near the wrist area.	
	Your finger should now be on the tendon of the palmaris longus.	
5	Deep to this tendon is a longitudinal muscle call the flexor digitorum superficialis. You can see part of this muscle on either side of that tendon.	**Flexor digitorum superficialis**
6	Deep to the flexor digitorum superficialis (near the wrist area) is a transverse muscle called the pronator quadratus.	**Pronator quadratus**
	In the wrist area, there is a broad ligament-like tissue that goes transversally across the wrist. This band holds some of the arm tendons in position. This is the **flexor retinaculum**. This is not a muscle.	
7	Go to the antecubital area. There is a short muscle that extends obliquely from the radius to the medial epicondyle of the humerus. This is the pronator teres.	**Pronator teres**

Table 5B-2   Lower Arm Muscles (continued)

	POSITION DESCRIPTION	MUSCLE
8	Find the extensor digitorum muscle on the posterior lower arm.	**Extensor digitorum**
	Move your finger to the proximal end near the elbow.	
9	Move your finger lateral. Your finger should be on the extensor carpi radialis longus.	**Extensor carpi radialis longus**
10	Between the extensor digitorum and the extensor carpi radialis longus is the extensor carpi radialis brevis.	**Extensor carpi radialis brevis**
	Go to the distal end of the extensor digitorum near the wrist area.	
	Move lateral and you will see two muscles that run oblique to the arm.	
11	The oblique muscle that is the most inferior is the extensor pollicis brevis.	**Extensor pollicis brevis**
12	The oblique muscle that is the most superior is the abductor pollicis longus.	**Abductor pollicis longus**
	Go back to the center of the extensor digitorum.	
13	Move medal and your finger should be on the extensor carpi ulnaris.	**Extensor carpi ulnaris**
	Move to the proximal end of the extensor carpi ulnaris	
14	You will see a muscle that extends obliquely from the lateral epicondyle of the humerus to the lateral edge of the olecranon process. This is the anconeus muscle.	**Anconeus**
	Move to the wrist area.	
	You will see a band of ligament-like tissue that extends transversally across the tendons of the arm muscles. This is the **extensor retinaculum**. This is not a muscle.	

Table 5B-3   Hand Muscles

	POSITION DESCRIPTION	MUSCLE
	Look at the palm of the hand.	
1	On the thumb side, there is a group of muscles collectively called the thenar muscles.	Thenar
	There are two muscles making up the thenar group.	
2	The most lateral thenar muscle is the abductor pollicis brevis.	Abductor pollicis brevis
3	The medial thenar muscle is the flexor pollicis brevis.	Flexor pollicis brevis
4	Deep to the thenar muscles is the opponens pollicis.	Opponens pollicis
5	Medial to the flexor pollicis brevis is the adductor pollicis.	Adductor pollicis
6	On the little finger side, there is a group of muscles collectively called the hypothenar muscles.	Hypothenar
	There are two muscles making up the hypothenar group.	
7	The most lateral hypothenar muscle is the flexor digiti minimi.	Flexor digiti minimi
8	The most medial hypothenar muscle is the abductor digiti minimi	Abductor digiti minimi

EXERCISE 5B-2 PALPATING MUSCLES

The following is a partial list of muscles that you can feel on your body. You should be able to palpate these muscles and others after studying muscle identification.

Biceps brachii: flex your arm a bit to feel the tendon angling medial.

Triceps brachii

Brachioradialis: you can feel this just a bit inferior to the elbow area on the lateral side.

Palmaris longus: close to the wrist area, you can feel the tendon of the palmaris longus.

EXERCISE 5B-3 THE NAMES OF MUSCLES

This exercise is designed to help you understand the naming process of a few select muscles. Below are 10 muscles of the human body. Each name or parts of the names is in reference to one of the following criterion:

Action

Shape

Site of origin or insertion

Number of origins

Location relative to a nearby bone (name the bone)

Direction the muscle fibers are oriented

Size

Location relative to a superficial area (name the area)

You are to use one or more of the items listed above that are involved in the name of the muscle. Below is an example to show you what this is all about:

Triceps brachii: Triceps: Number of origins

                        Brachii: Location relative to a superficial area (brachium)

Biceps brachii	Biceps	
	brachii	
Palmaris longus	Palmaris	
	longus	
Flexor digitorum superficialis	Flexor	
	Digitorum	
	Superficialis	
Brachioradialis	Brachio	
	Radialis	
Adductor pollicis	Adductor	
	pollicis	
Deltoid	Deltoid	

PRONUNCIATION

1	Anconeus (an-koe-nee-us)		10	Hallucis (haa-loo-sis)
2	Biceps brachii (by-seps bray-kee-eye)		11	Opponens (oh-poe-nins)
3	Brachialis (bray-kee-al-is)		12	Palmaris (paul-mare-is)
4	Brachioradialis (bray-kee-oh-ray-dee-al-is)		13	Pollicis (paul-i-sis)
5	Brevis (breh-vis)		14	Pronator teres (pro-nay-tor tare-eez)
6	Coracobrachialis (kor-uh-koe-bray-kee-al-is)		15	Quadratus (kwah-dray-tus)
7	Flexor carpi (flex-or kar-pee)		16	Superficialis (soo-per-fish-ee-al-is)
8	Flexor digiti minimi (di-ji-tee min-i-mee)		17	Thenar (thee-nar)
9	Flexor digitorum (fex-or di-ji-tor-um)		18	Triceps brachii (try-seps bray-kee-eye)

CHAPTER 5C   THE UPPER APPENDICULAR REGION

BLOOD VESSELS

This lab session involves the study of the blood vessels that supply the upper arm. The blood vessels going to the arms arise from the subclavian arteries. The arteries generally have the same name as the bone they are near. Regarding the arms; there are more veins than arteries. The radial vein and ulnar vein are deep veins while the cephalic and basilic veins are superficial.

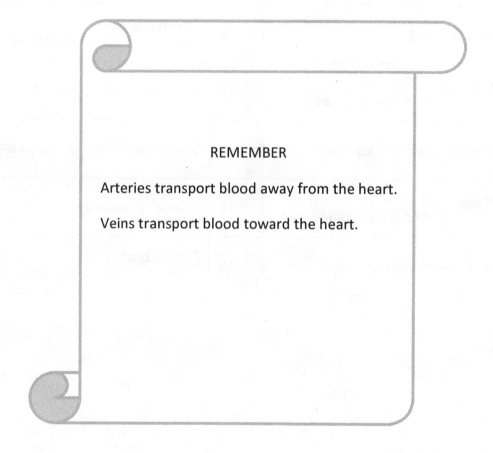

REMEMBER

Arteries transport blood away from the heart.

Veins transport blood toward the heart.

EXERCISE 5C-1   IDENTIFICATION OF BLOOD VESSELS

The best way to study the blood vessels is to look at a model or a diagram and put your finger on one blood vessel and trace the flow of blood with your finger. For example, put your finger on a subclavian artery and follow it to the axillary artery then to the brachial artery.

Table 5C-1   Blood Vessels (arteries)

Aortic arch		Aortic arch	
Brachiocephalic artery			
R. subclavian a		L. subclavian a	
R. axillary a		L. axillary a	
Brachial a		Brachial a	
Radial a	Radial a	Radial a	Ulnar a

Table 5C-2   Blood Vessels (veins)

L.Radial v	L.Ulnar v	R.Radial v	R.Ulnar v
Brachial v		Brachial v	
Axillary v		Axillary v	
L. subclavian v		R. subclavian v	
L. brachiocephalic v		R. brachiocephalic v	
Superior Vena Cava			
Right Atrium of the Heart			

Table 5C-3   Blood Vessels (veins)

L. Cephalic v (se-fal-ic)	L. Basilic v (buh-sil-ic)	R. Cephalic v	R. Basilic v
	Axillary v		Axillary v
L. subclavian v	L. subclavian v	R. subclavian v	R. subclavian v
L. brachiocephalic v	L. brachiocephalic v	R. brachiocephalic v	R. brachiocephalic v
Superior Vena Cava			
Right Atrium of the Heart			

Table 5C-4   Blood Vessels (veins)

L. cephalic v	R. cephalic v
L. median cubital v	R. median cubital v
L. basilic v	R. basilic v
L. axillary v	R. axillary v
L. subclavian v	R. subclavian v
L. brachiocephalic v	R. brachiocephalic v
Superior Vena Cava	
Right Atrium of the Heart	

CHAPTER 5D   THE UPPER APPENDICULAR REGION

THE NERVES

The nerves of the upper appendicular region arise from the brachial plexus. The brachial plexus innervates the pectoral girdle and the upper limb (brachium and antebrachium). The nerves discussed here arise from C-8 to T-1. There are several nerves associated with the brachial plexus but the ones discussed in this class are:

1. Ulnar nerve
2. Radial nerve
3. Median nerve

While examining pictures of the brachial plexus, examine table 5D-1.

Table 5D-1   Nerves of the Upper Appendage

Nerve	Description	Function
Ulnar nerve	This nerve runs along the medial side of the humerus, near the medial epicondyle of the humerus to the wrist and hand.	This nerve innervates the medial aspect of the wrist and digits on the anterior and posterior sides. It specifically innervates digit 5 and the medial half of digit 4.
Radial nerve	This nerve passes along the posterior aspect of the humerus about the region of the axilla to continue along the lateral edge to the wrist and hand.	This nerve innervates mainly the lateral, posterior hand, including digits 1, 2, 3, and a portion of 4.
Median nerve	This nerve passes long the anterior aspect of the humerus, down the center of the antebrachium to the wrist and hand.	This nerve innervates mainly the lateral, anterior hand, including digits 1, 2, 3, and a portion of 4.

CHAPTER 5E   THE UPPER APPENDICULAR REGION

THE ARTICULATIONS (SHOULDER AND ELBOW JOINTS)

An articulation (joint) is the place of contact between two bones, between a bone and cartilage or between bone and teeth. Bones are said to articulate with each other. The study of joints is called arthrology (arthron = joint and logos = study).

Joints can be classified according to the extent of movement (see table 5E-1). Joints can also be classified according to their structure (see table 5E-2).

Located in the lab room are models of the shoulder and elbow joints. Table 5E-3 lists the names of the ligaments of select joints for you to identify. Use your textbook to verify the identification of the ligaments.

ARTICULATIONS

EXERCISE 5E-1 CLASSIFICATION OF JOINTS

Table 5E-1 **Classification Based on Movement**

Joint Classification	Characteristic	Example
Synarthrosis	Immoveable joint	Skull sutures
Amphiarthrosis	Slightly moveable joint	Joint between the vertebral bodies Joint between the sacrum and L5
Diarthrosis	Freely moveable joint	Shoulder, elbow, hip, knee

Table 5E-2 **Classification Based on Structure**

Joint Classification	Characteristic	Example
Fibrous	Ligamentous connection between two bones	Joint between tibia and fibula Skull sutures
Cartilaginous	Pad of cartilage between the bones	Pubic symphysis Intervertebral discs
Synovial	Cavity within the joint is filled with fluid (synovial fluid)	Shoulder, elbow, hip, knee

EXERCISE 5E-2 IDENTIFICATION OF LIGAMENTS

Table 5E-3   The Joints (Ligaments)

Shoulder joint	Extending from the clavicle to the coracoid	coracoclavicular ligament
	Extending from the clavicle to the acromion	acromioclavicular ligament
	Extending from the acromion to the coracoid	coracoacromial ligament
	Extending from the head of the humerus to the glenoid fossa	glenohumeral ligament
Elbow joint	Extending from the humerus to the radius on the lateral side	radial collateral ligament
	Extending from the humerus to the ulna on the medial side	ulnar collateral ligament
	Extending from the ulna to (and around) the head of the radius	annular ligament

CHAPTER 6   THE LOWER APPENDAGE

Chapter 6 discusses the structures associated with the lower appendage, which includes the pelvis (os coxa), upper leg (called the thigh), lower leg (called the leg), and the ankle and foot. Chapter 6 is divided into different sections as indicated below:

6A: bones and bone structures of the lower appendage

6B: muscles of the lower appendage

6C: blood vessels of the lower appendage

6D: nerves of the lower appendage (lumbar and sacral plexus)

6E: ligaments of the hip joint and the knee joint

The material used in this lab will be (but not limited to):

Models of the lower skeleton (disarticulated)

Models of male and female pelves

Fully articulated skeleton

Thigh and leg muscle models

Thigh and leg blood vessel models

Textbook images of the lumbar and sacral plexus

Models of the hip and knee joint

CHAPTER 6A THE LOWER APPENDICULAR REGION

THE APPENDICULAR SKELETON (PELVIC GIRDLE AND ITS APPENDAGE)

The second division of the appendicular skeleton is the *pelvic girdle*. The pelvic girdle consists of the hip, which is made of two major structures called the *coxa*. Each coxa (os coxa) is made of three bones fused together. The three bones are ilium, ischium, and pubis. This chapter deals with the pelvic girdle and its appendages.

Just as we did in the last chapter, we will study in detail the various landmarks associated with the hips, legs, ankles, and foot bones. You will find that these bones are much larger than the bones of the arms and the various landmarks (muscle attachments) are generally larger than those of the arms.

The bones of the lower extremities must support the weight of the upper body. This requires a great deal of strength. To meet the demands needed to support the lower body, not only are the structures larger but the fossa are even deeper. For example, compare the depression of the glenoid fossa with the depression of the acetabular fossa.

There are 206 bones

in the human body

EXERCISE 6A-1 IDENTIFICATION OF SKELETAL BONES AND
BONE STRUCTURES

At your lab table you have a box of a complete disarticulated skeleton. The information in tables 6A-1 through 6A-7 will help guide you as you identify skeletal structures. Use your textbook figures to help you verify the structures. Be sure to examine the skeleton that is hanging in the middle of lab room.

Table 6A-1   The Os Coxa

1	ilium	This is the major part of the os coxa.
2	iliac crest	The superior crest of the ilium.
3	greater sciatic notch	Follow the iliac crest to the posterior side. You will see a huge notch.
4	posterior inferior iliac spine	The superior edge of the greater sciatic notch.
5	posterior superior iliac spine	The inferior edge of the greater sciatic notch.
6	ischial spine	The inferior edge of the greater sciatic notch.
7	lesser sciatic notch	This is a notch immediately inferior to the ischial spine.
8	anterior superior iliac spine	Follow the iliac crest to the anterior side. You will find a bump.
9	anterior inferior iliac spine	The bulge immediately inferior to the anterior superior iliac spine.

Table 6A-1   The Os Coxa   (continued)

10	obturator foramen	This is a large hole associated with the coxa.
11	pubis	Anterior to the obturator foramen.
12	ischium	Posterior to the obturator foramen.
13	acetabulum (acetabular fossa)	This is a huge fossa on the lateral edge of the coxa.

The head of the femur pivots in the acetabulum.
Huge muscles pass through the obturator foramen.
Each os coxa is made of three major parts: ilium, ischium, and pubis.
The ischium consists of the ischial tuberosity, which we sit on.
The pelvic inlet is the space between the left and right pelvic brim.
The pelvic outlet is the space between the left and right ischial spines.

Table 6A-2   The Femur

1	head	At the proximal end, medial side of the femur is a huge rounded bulge.
2	greater trochanter	Lateral to the head is a huge bulge.
3	lesser trochanter	Inferior to the head (just a smidget) and on the medial side.
4	neck	The area between the head and the greater trochanter.
5	fovea capitis	This is a depression in the center of head of the femur. Sometimes called the **fovea for ligament of the head**.
6	lateral condyle	At the distal end (on the posterior side) you will find two rounded condyles. This is the condyle that appears to be in line with the greater trochanter.
7	medial condyle	This is the condyle (on the posterior side) that appears to be in line with the head of the femur.
8	intercondylar fossa	The depression between the two condyles.
9	lateral epicondyle	The bulge that is lateral to the lateral condyle.
10	medial epicondyle	The bulge that is medial to the medial condyle.
11	linea aspera	On the posterior side, you can feel a ridge that runs down the center of the length of the femur.

Table 6A-3   The Tibia

1	patella	This is a sesmoid bone that protects the joint at the femur and tibia.
2	intercondylar tubercles	On the superior, tip edge of the tibia, there are two small, bony projections. Sometimes they are called intercondylar eminence.
3	tibial tuberosity	A bulge located at the proximal end and on the anterior side of the tibia.
4	medial malleolus	A knobby bulge at the distal, medial end of the tibia.
5	anterior margin	Run your finger along the anterior edge of the tibia. You will feel a "sharp" ridge running the length of the tibia.

Table 6A-4   The Fibula

1	lateral malleolus	A knobby bulge at the distal, lateral end of the fibula
The lateral malleolus and medial malleolus partially protect the talus of the ankle.		

Table 6A-5   The Tarsals

1	talus	The tibia sits on the talus.
2	calcaneus	Sitting partially posterior to the talus is our heel bone.
3	navicular	Anterior to the talus.
4	medial cuneiform intermediate cuneiform lateral cuneiform	Anterior to the navicular are three cuneiform bones.
5	cuboid	Lateral to the lateral cuneiform.
6	calcaneal tendon	There is a tendon that is attached to the calcaneus and a muscle called the gastrocnemius (calf muscle). According to Greek Mythology, this tendon is known as the Achilles tendon. In anatomy, this tendon is anatomically known as the calcaneal tendon.

Table 6A-6   The Metatarsals

1	**metatarsal number 1**	The most medial metatarsal (in line with the big toe).
2	**metatarsal number 2**	The metatarsal in line with the toe that is lateral to the hallux.
3	**metatarsal number 3**	The metatarsal in line with the toe that is lateral again.
4	**metatarsal number 4**	The metatarsal in line with the toe that is lateral again.
5	**metatarsal number 5**	The metatarsal in line with the little toe.

Table 6A-7   The Phalanges

1	**proximal and distal phalanges**	The hallux has two phalanges.
2	**proximal, middle, and distal phalanges**	All other digits have three phalanges.
The big toe (hallux) is digit number 1.		

EXERCISE 6A-2   PALPATING BONE STRUCTURES

The following is a partial list of bone structures that you can feel on your body. You should be able to palpate these structures and others after studying bone identification.

Greater trochanter

Patella

Medial and lateral epicondyles of the femur

Tibial tuberosity

Anterior margin of the tibia

Medial and lateral malleolus

Calcaneus

EXERCISE 6A-3   COMPARISON OF MALE AND FEMALE HIP STRUCTURES

The individual bone structures are the same for male and female but there are modifications in the female hips to prepare the female for childbearing. There are many differences in the overall structure of the male and female hip but in this class we will discuss two major differences.

1. The pubic arch (the fusion of the two pubis bones by the pubic symphysis) is much wider in the female than in the male.
2. The coccyx and sacrum are much straighter in the female than in the male.

The combination of the two differences creates a wider pelvic outlet, which makes it a little easier for vaginal birth of a child.

There are times when a female's coccyx is curved anteriorly as in the male pelvis thus causing difficulty in childbirth. In this scenario, many times the child passing through the narrowed pelvic outlet will break the mother's coccyx bone.

Your instructor will demonstrate with a fetal skull, the birth of a child through the female pelvic outlet and the birth of a child through a pelvic outlet that is much smaller as is the case of a male pelvic outlet.

In this exercise, compare the models of the male and female pelvic girdle.

EXERCISE 6A-4   EXAMINATION OF THE COMPLETE SKELETON

Examine the skeleton that is hanging in the center of the lab room. Table 6A-8 indicates some things to specifically examine while looking at the skeleton.

Table 6A-8   Examination of the Skeleton

1. Observe how the femur sits in the acetabulum.

2. Observe the positioning of the patella.

3. Observe that the tibia sits on the talus.

4. Examine the size of the calcaneus.

5. Notice the positioning of the lateral and medial malleolus. Those two structures partially protect the ankle.

PRONUNCIATION

1	Acetabulum (aa-se-tab-you-lum)	12	Linea aspera (lin-ee-uh as-pair-uh)
2	Calcaneus (kal-kane-ee-us)	13	Malleolus (muh-lee-uh-lus)
3	Condyle (kon-dyle)	14	Metatarsal (meh-tu-tar-sul)
4	Cuboid (kew-boyd)	15	Navicular (nuh-vik-you-lar)
5	Cuneiform (kew-nee-form)	16	Obturator (ob-ter-ay-tore)
6	Epicondyle (eh-pi-kon-dile)	17	Os coxa (oz coks-uh)
7	Fibula (fib-you-la)	18	Phalanges (fuh-lan-jees)
8	Fovea capitis (foe-vee-uh kap-i-tis)	19	Pubis (pew-bis)
9	Ilium (ill-ee-um)	20	Sciatic (sigh-aa-tik)
10	Intercondylar (in-ter-kon-deh-lar)	21	Talus (taa-lus)
11	Ischial (isk-ee-ul)	22	Trochanter (troe-kan-ter)

CHAPTER 6B   THE LOWER APPENDICULAR REGION

SKELETAL MUSCLES

While studying the muscles, you will find that many have names that are similar to the name of the bone they are on.

In this class we study not only the names of muscles but the origin, insertion, and action of the muscles. These topics will be studied in lecture rather than in the laboratory setting.

We will study at least 64 muscles of the lower appendage

Exercise 6B-1 Identification of Skeletal Muscles

Table 6B-1   Upper Leg Muscles

	POSITION DESCRIPTION	MUSCLE
1	Find the sartorius muscle on the anterior side of the upper leg.	**Sartorius**
	Go to the distal end of the sartorius near the patella region.	
2	Go lateral and your finger will be on the vastus medialis.	**Vastus medialis**
3	Go lateral and your finger will be on the rectus femoris.	**Rectus femoris**
4	Go lateral one more time and you will find the vastus lateralis. Deep to the iliotibial tract is a portion of the vastus lateralis.	**Vastus lateralis**
5	Deep to the rectus femoris is the vastus intermedius.	**Vastus intermedius**
	The vastus lateralis, vastus medialis, vastus intermedius, and rectus femoris are collectively called the quadriceps. Quadriceps is not a muscle name.	
6	Find the gracilis muscle. It is the most medial muscle of the upper leg.	**Gracilis**
	There are three muscles we study located between gracilis and the sartorius.	
	Go to the center of the gracilis and move your finger laterally toward the superior end of the sartorius.	
7	The first muscle lateral to the gracilis is the adductor longus.	**Adductor longus**
8	Move lateral again is the pectineus muscle.	**Pectineus**
	Move lateral again and you will find a vein, artery, and nerve.	
9	Move lateral to the nerve and you will see the iliacus.	**Iliacus**

Table 6B-1   Upper Leg Muscles (continued)

	POSITION DESCRIPTION	MUSCLE
10	The iliacus muscle is many times combined with the psoas muscle, which is superior to the inguinal ligament area, and is therefore called the iliopsoas muscle.	**Iliopsoas**
11	Go lateral one more time and you will see the most lateral muscle of the thigh. This is a small muscle located on the lateral edge of the hip. This is the tensor fasciae latae muscle.	**Tensor fasciae latae**
The tensor fasciae latae muscle has a long and broad tendon that extends from it to the tibial tuberosity. This is the **iliotibial tract**. This is not a muscle. Deep to the IT band is the vastus lateralis muscle.		
Go to the posterior upper leg.		
Go to the junction of the gluteus maximus muscle, tensor fasciae latae, and iliotibial tract.		
12	Go medial and your finger should be on the biceps femoris.	**Biceps femoris**
The biceps femoris muscle is made of two parts.		
13	The long head of the biceps femoris is the major portion on the posterior upper leg.	**Long head**
14	The short head of the biceps femoris can be found deep to the long head and appears between the long head and the iliotibial tract at the distal end near the popliteal region.	**Short head**
15	Medial to the long head of the biceps femoris is the semitendinosus.	**Semitendinosus**
Notice the tendon of the biceps femoris angle lateral and the tendon of the semitendinosus angles medial both in the popliteal region.		
16	Deep to the semitendinosus is the semimembranosus.	**Semimembranosus**

Table 6B-1   Upper Leg Muscles (continued)

	POSITION DESCRIPTION	MUSCLE
	The semitendinosus, semimembranosus, and biceps femoris are collectively called the hamstrings.	
	The hamstrings are not a muscle name.	
	Go to the proximal portion of the semitendinosus and the gracilis muscles	
17	Between those muscles is the adductor magnus.	**Adductor magnus**
	Rotate the leg to view the medial side of the upper leg.	
	Find the gracilis muscle again and go toward the superior edge.	
	Move your finger anterior and you will find the adductor longus muscle.	
	Go back to the gracilis and move your finger posterior to find the adductor magnus muscle.	

Table 6B-2   Lower Leg Muscles

	POSITION DESCRIPTION	MUSCLE
1	Find the tibialis anterior muscle of the anterior lower leg.	**Tibialis anterior**
	This muscle begins at the patellar region and angles across the leg medially toward the hallux.	
2	Between the extensor digitorum longus and the tibialis anterior is the extensor hallucis longus.	**Extensor hallucis longus**
	Rotate the leg to view the medial side.	
	Go to the distal end of the tibia on the anterior side. If you go posterior to that area, you will see tendons of other leg muscles, a big space, and then you will see the calcaneal tendon (attached to the calcaneus).	
3	Go posterior to the tibial bone. The tendons are identified in this manner: posterior to the tibialis anterior is the tibialis posterior tendon.	**Tibialis posterior**
4	Posterior again is the flexor digitorum longus tendon	**Flexor digitorum longus**
	Posterior again and you will see an artery and a nerve	
5	Posterior again is the flexor hallucis longus muscle tendon.	**Flexor hallucis longus**
	The typical way to remember those structures is via the acronym; TD and H (Tom, Dick And Harry) Tibialis / Digitorum / Artery, Nerve / Hallucis	
	Rotate the leg to view the lateral side.	
6	Find the gastrocnemius (which is a posterior muscle).	**Gastrocnemius**
7	Move anterior (deep to the gastrocnemius) is the soleus.	**Soleus**

Table 6B-2   Lower Leg Muscles   (continued)

	POSITION DESCRIPTION	MUSCLE
	Move to the center of the soleus.	
8	Move anterior and your finger will be on the fibularis longus.	**Fibularis longus**
	The fibularis longus has a tendon that loops around the lateral malleolus.	
	Move to the distal end of the fibularis longus.	
9	Deep to the fibularis longus (but you can see part of the muscle anterior and posterior to the fibularis longus) is the fibularis brevis.	**Fibularis brevis**
10	Anterior to the fibularis brevis is the extensor digitorum longus muscle.	**Extensor digitorum longus**
11	Between the extensor digitorum longus and the tibialis anterior is the extensor hallucis longus.	**Extensor hallucis longus**
	At the distal end of the tibialis anterior, you will see a ligament-like tissue that surrounds the tendons of the lower leg muscles. This is the superior and inferior extensor retinaculum. These are not muscles.	
	The superior retinaculum runs transversally across the ankle area.	
	The inferior retinaculum also runs transversally but divides to form two parts.	
	Go back to the posterior lower leg and find the gastrocnemius again.	
12	The gastrocnemius consist of two parts; the medial and lateral heads.	**Medial and lateral head**
	The two heads merge together to from the calcaneal tendon that attaches to the calcaneus.	

Table 6B-2   Lower Leg Muscles   (continued)

		POSITION DESCRIPTION	MUSCLE
		Move to the popliteal region of the leg.	
13		Immediately superior to the superior edge of the lateral head of the gastrocnemius is the plantaris. The plantaris actually has a long tendon that runs deep to the gastrocnemius all the way to the calcaneus.	**Plantaris**
	Deep to the soleus are the following muscles: tibialis posterior and flexor hallucis longus.		
14		Posterior to the tibialis posterior is the flexor digitorum longus.	**Flexor digitorum longus**

Table 6B-3   Foot Muscles

		POSITION DESCRIPTION	MUSCLE
	On the plantar side of the foot, there are three major groups of superficial muscles.		
1		The group of muscles in the center of the sole of the foot is flexor digitorum brevis muscles.	**Flexor digitorum brevis**
2		Lateral to the flexor digitorum brevis group is the abductor digiti minimi group.	**Abductor digiti minimi**
3		Medial to the flexor digitorum brevis group is the abductor hallucis group.	**Abductor hallucis**
	The superficial covering of the bottom of the foot is the plantar aponeurosis.		

EXERCISE 6B-2 IDENTIFICATION OF SKELETAL MUSCLES OF THE HIP

Table 6B-4   Muscles of the Hip

	POSITION DESCRIPTION	MUSCLE
1	Go to the gluteus maximus muscle.	**Gluteus maximus**
2	Deep to the gluteus maximus is the gluteus medius.	**Gluteus medius**
3	Deep to the gluteus medius is the gluteus minimus.	**Gluteus minimus**
4	Inferior to the gluteus minimus is the piriformis.	**Piriformis**
5	Inferior again is the superior gemellus.	**Superior gemellus**
6	Inferior again is the obturator internus.	**Obturator internus**
7	Inferior one more time is the inferior gemellus.	**Inferior gemellus**
8	Inferior one last time is the quadratus femoris.	**Quadratus femoris**

EXERCISE 6B-3   PALPATING MUSCLES

The following is a partial list of muscles that you can feel on your body. You should be able to palpate these muscles and others after studying muscle identification.

Tensor fasciae latae: abduct your upper leg and feel the tensor fasciae latae tense a bit.

Semitendinosus and biceps femoris: flex your lower leg. In the popliteal region you can feel the tendons of these two muscles.

Gastrocnemius: you can also feel the calcaneal tendon associated with the gastrocnemius.

EXERCISE 6B-4 THE NAMES OF MUSCLES

This exercise is designed to help you understand the naming process of a few select muscles. Below are 10 muscles of the human body. Each name or parts of the names is in reference to one of the following criterion:

Action

Shape

Site of origin or insertion

Number of origins

Location relative to a nearby bone (name the bone)

Direction the muscle fibers are oriented

Size

Location relative to a superficial area (name the area)

You are to use one or more of the items listed above that are involved in the name of the muscle. Below is an example to show you what this is all about:

Triceps brachii: Triceps: Number of origins

Brachii: Location relative to a superficial area (brachium)

Adductor magnus	Adductor	
	Magnus	
Vastus lateralis	Vastus	
	Lateralis	
Biceps femoris	Biceps	
	Femoris	
Fibularis longus	Fibularis	
	longus	
Semimembranosus	semimembranosus	
Vastus lateralis	Vastus	
	lateralis	
Adductor longus	Adductor	
	longus	

Pronunciation

1	Brevis (breh-vis)		11	Plantaris (plan-tare-is)
2	Flexor digiti minimi (di-ji-tee min-i-mee)		12	Quadriceps (kwa-dri-seps)
3	Flexor digitorum (fex-or di-ji-tor-um)		13	Sartorius (sar-tor-ee-us)
4	Frontalis (frun-tal-is)		14	Semimembranosus (sem-ee-mem-bruh-no-sus)

5	Gastrocnemius
	          (gas-truk-nee-mee-us)
			15	Semitendinosus
				          (sem-ee-ten-din-oh-sus)

6	Gracilis (graa-si-lis)		16	Soleus (so-lee-us)
7	Hallucis (haa-loo-sis)		17	Tensor fasciae latae (ten-sor fay-she-ee lay-tuh)
8	Iliacus (ill-ee-ak-us)		18	Tibialis (ti-bee-al-is)
9	Iliopsoas (ill-ee-oh-so-az)		19	Vastus (vas-tus)
10	Pectineus (pek-tin-ee-us)		20	Vastus intermedius (in-ter-mee-dee-us)

CHAPTER 6C   THE LOWER APPENDICULAR REGION

BLOOD VESSELS

This lab session involves the study of the blood vessels that supply the lower appendage. The blood vessels going to the legs arise indirectly from the descending aorta. The descending aorta branches to form the common iliac arteries. The common iliac artery forms the external and internal iliac arteries.

In this class, we will study the blood vessels that arise from the external iliac artery to the femoral artery, etc.

The arteries generally have the same name as the bone they are near. Regarding the legs; there are more veins than arteries.

REMEMBER

Arteries transport blood away from the heart.

Veins transport blood toward the heart.

Veins have valves along their length, which helps in the movement of blood back to the heart.

Exercise 6C-1   Identification of Blood Vessels

Table 6C-1   Blood Vessels (arteries)

Common iliac artery	
External iliac a	
Femoral a	
Popliteal a	
Anterior tibial a	Posterior tibial a (also branches to form the fibular a)

Table 6C-2   Blood Vessels (veins)

Anterior tibial v	Fibular v joins the posterior tibial v	Great saphenous v
Popliteal v		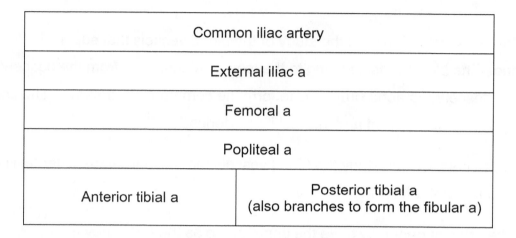
Femoral v		
External iliac v		
Common iliac v		
Inferior vena cava		
Right atrium of the heart		

CHAPTER 6D   THE LOWER APPENDICULAR REGION

THE NERVES

The nerves of the lower appendicular region arise from the lumbar and the sacral plexus. These plexuses innervate the pelvic girdle and the lower limb (os coxa and the lower appendages). The nerves associated with the lumbar plexus arise from T1 through L 4. The nerves associated with the sacral plexus arise from L 4 through S 4.

There are several nerves associated with the lumbar and sacral plexus but the ones discussed in this class are:

> Lumbar plexus: 1. Femoral nerve
>   2. Saphenous nerve
> Sacral plexus: 1. Sciatic nerve
>   2. Pudendal nerve

While examining pictures of the lumbar plexus and sacral plexus, examine table 6D-1.

Table 6D-1   Nerves of the Lower Appendage   (Lumbar Plexus)

Nerve	Description	Function
Femoral nerve	This nerve runs along the anterior thigh and branches many times.	This nerve innervates the sartorius muscle and the quadriceps.
Saphenous nerve	This nerve runs along the medial aspect of the thigh and the lower leg.	This nerve innervates the skin of the upper and lower leg on the medial side.

Table 6D-2   Nerves of the Lower Appendage (Sacral Plexus)

Nerve	Description	Function
Sciatic nerve	This nerve runs along the posterior femur, between the femoral condyles and then branches to form a tibial nerve and fibular nerve.	Innervates the hamstrings. The fibular portion innervates the majority of the foot. The tibial portion innervates the "heel" and "ball" of the foot.
Pudendal nerve	This nerve parallels the sciatic nerve as far as the ischial tuberosity.	Innervates the following: perineal muscles anal muscles urethral sphincter muscles external genitalia muscles bulbospongiosus muscles ischiocavernosus muscles

CHAPTER 6E   THE LOWER APPENDICULAR REGION

THE ARTICULATIONS (HIP AND KNEE JOINTS)

An articulation (joint) is the place of contact between two bones, between a bone and cartilage or between bone and teeth. Bones are said to articulate with each other. The study of joints is called arthrology (arthron = joint and logos = study).

Located in the lab room are models of the hip and knee joints. Table 6E-3 lists the names of the ligaments of select joints for you to identify. Use your textbook to verify the identification of the ligaments.

ARTICULATIONS

EXERCISE 6E-1 IDENTIFICATION OF LIGAMENTS

Table 6E-1 The Joints (Ligaments)

Hip joint	Extending from the acetabular rim in the ilium region to the femur	**iliofemoral ligament**
	Extending from the acetabular rim in the pubis region to the femur	**pubofemoral ligament**
	Extending from the acetabular rim in the ischial region to the femur	**ischiofemoral ligament**
	Extending from the inside of the acetabular fossa to the fovea capitis of the femur	**ligamentum teres**
Knee joint	Extending from the lateral epicondyle of the femur to the fibula	**fibular collateral ligament (lateral collateral)**
	Extending from the medial epicondyle of the femur to the tibia	**tibial collateral (medial collateral)**
	Extending from the superior portion of the tibia to the medial edge of the intercondylar fossa of the femur	**posterior cruciate ligament (PCL)**
	Extending from the superior portion of the tibia to the lateral edge of the intercondylar fossa of the femur	**anterior cruciate ligament (ACL)**
	Extending from the patella to the tibial tuberosity	**patellar ligament**
	Extending from the lateral and medial edge of the patella to the superior portion of the tibia	**patellar retinaculae**
Not a ligament	A pair of cartilage pads sandwiched between the medial and lateral condyles of the femur and the superior surface of the tibia	**medial and lateral menisci (meniscus --- singular)**

CHAPTER 7   THE TORSO REGION

Chapter 7 discusses the structures associated with the torso, which includes the anterior torso and the posterior torso. Chapter 7 is divided into different sections as indicated below:

>7A: rib bones, sternum, and vertebrae
>
>7B: anterior and posterior muscles
>
>$7C_1$: the heart
>
>$7C_2$: the blood vessels
>
>7D: nerves of the torso (spinal cord)
>
>7E: lungs
>
>7F: abdominal organs

The material used in this lab will be (but not limited to):

Models of the torso skeleton

Models of torso muscles

Models of torso blood vessels

Models of the lungs

Models of the digestive organs

Microscope slides showing a transverse view of the spinal cord

Dissected cat showing torso organs

Dissected cat showing abdominal organs

Dissected stomach showing rugae

Dissected intestines showing villi

Model showing the spinal cord

CHAPTER 7A   THE TORSO REGION

THE THORACIC CAGE AND VERTEBRAE

It was mentioned in a previous chapter that the entire skeletal system could be divided into two divisions, the axial and appendicular divisions. The axial division consists of the skull and its associated bones, the thoracic cage, and the vertebral column. The axial division is made of 80 bones. The appendicular skeleton consists of the appendages and their associated bones, which are made of 126 bones. This chapter is concerned with the axial division, primarily the thoracic cage and the vertebrae.

The thoracic cage is made of the sternum and the ribs. The sternum consists of three bones, the manubrium, body, and xiphoid. There are 12 pairs of ribs of which 7 pair have a direct articulation with the sternum, 3 pair have an indirect articulation with the sternum, and 2 pair have no articulation with the sternum. The first 7pair (ribs 1-7) are called **vertebrosternal** ribs. The next 3 pair (ribs 8,9, and 10) are called **vertebrochondral** ribs and the last 2 pair (ribs 11 and 12) are called **vertebral** (floating) ribs. All ribs have an articulation with the thoracic vertebrae.

There are 24 individual vertebrae making up the vertebral column. The first 7 are called the **cervical** vertebrae, the next 12 are called the **thoracic** vertebrae, and the final 5 are called the **lumbar** vertebrae. The sacrum is attached to the lumbar vertebrae. It is actually made of 5 fused vertebrae. The coccyx is attached to the sacrum. It is made of 3 to 5 fused vertebrae. The coccyx forms the "tailbone".

EXERCISE 7A-1   THE STUDY OF BONES AND BONE STRUCTURES OF THE THORACIC REGION

THE STERNUM

At your lab table you have a model of the sternum and several representative individual vertebrae and a complete vertebral column. The information in tables 7A-1 through 7A-4 will help guide you as you identify vertebral structures. Use your textbook figures to help you verify the structures.

Table 7A-1   The Sternum

	Bone or bone structure	Description of the location
1	**Manubrium**	The superior portion of the sternum. Only one pair of ribs attach to the manubrium.
2	**Jugular notch**	The curved area at the superior edge of the manubrium.
3	**Body**	The main portion of the sternum. Ribs 2 through 7 directly attach to the body.
4	**Xiphoid process**	The terminal structure located at the distal end of the body. Ribs do not attach to the xiphoid.

Table 7A-2   The Vertebrae

	Bone structure	Description of the location
1	**Vertebral foramen**	The huge hole in the vertebra. The spinal cord passes through this foramen.
2	**Body**	Anterior to the vertebral foramen is the solid portion of the vertebra.
3	**Spinous process**	Posterior to the vertebral foramen is a spine-like structure
4	**Transverse processes**	There are bony structures that extend laterally from the vertebral foramen area.
5	**Lamina**	This is the curved area between the transverse process and the spinous process.
6	**Pedicle**	This is the "stem" between the transverse process and the body.
7	**Dens**	Vertebra number 2 (**axis**) has an anterior structure that protrudes upward from the body of the vertebra. The **atlas** (vertebra number 1) pivots on the dens.
8	**Transverse foramen**	Only the seven cervical vertebrae have 2 holes in addition to the vertebral foramen. The vertebral artery passes through these holes. They are located within the transverse processes.

Table 7A-3   The Rib Cage

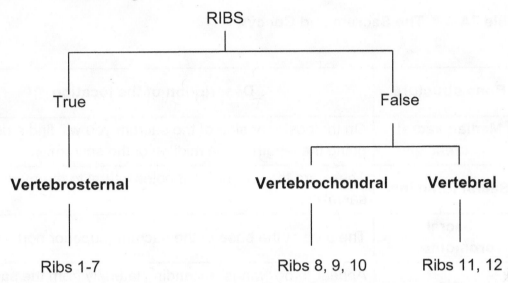

Rib number 1 has cartilage that attaches to the manubrium of the sternum.

Ribs 2, 3, 4, 5, 6, and 7 have cartilage that attaches to the body of the sternum.

Therefore, ribs 1-7 have a direct attachment from the vertebrae to the sternum ("sternal").

Rib 8 has cartilage that attaches to the cartilage of rib 7.

Rib 9 has cartilage that attaches to the cartilage of rib 8.

Rib 10 has cartilage that attaches to the cartilage of rib 9.

Therefore, ribs 8-10 have attachment to the vertebrae and to the cartilage of the rib above them ("chondral").

Ribs 11 and 12 do not have any attachment to the sternum, hence the term "vertebral" only.

Table 7A-4   The Sacrum and Coccyx

	Bone structure	Description of the location
1	**Median sacral crest**	On the posterior side of the sacrum you will find a ridge going the length of the midline of the sacrum.
2	**Sacral foramina**	These are the four pairs of holes lateral to the median sacral crest.
3	**Sacral promontory**	The area at the base of the sacrum (superior portion).
4	**Ala**	Appear to be "wings" extending laterally from the sacral promontory.
5	**Sacral hiatus**	This is the inferior end of the sacral canal. (inferior to the median sacral crest)
6	**Coccyx**	This pointy bone connects to the inferior portion of the sacrum called the apex.

EXERCISE 7A-2:   PALPATION OF VERTEBRAL STRUCTURES

Stand behind your partner. Run your finger down the spinous processes of the vertebrae. See if you can feel the spinous process of vertebra number 7. It typically protrudes out a bit farther than the other spinous processes.

PRONUNCIATION

1	Ala (ay-luh)		8	Pedicle (peh-di-cul)	
2	Cervical (sir-vi-cul)		9	Spinous (spy-nus)	
3	Coccyx (kok-siks)		10	Vertebrae (ver-teh-bray)	
4	Dens (denz)		11	Vertebral (ver-teh-brul)	
5	Hiatus (high-ay-tus)		12	Vertebrochondral (ver-teh-broe-kon-drul)	
6	Lamina (laa-mi-nuh)		13	Vertebrosternal (ver-teh-broe-ster-nul)	
7	Manubrium (muh-new-bree-um)		14	Xiphoid (zif-oyd) (not a long i sound)	

CHAPTER 7B   THE TORSO REGION

MUSCLES OF THE TORSO

EXERCISE 7B-1 IDENTIFICATION OF SKELETAL MUSCLES

Table 7B-1   Torso Muscles

	POSITION DESCRIPTION	MUSCLE
1	Lateral to the sternum are the pectoralis major muscles	**Pectoralis major**
2	Lateral to the pectoralis major are the shoulder muscles.	**Deltoid**
3	Covering the anterior abdomen is the rectus abdominis.	**Rectus abdominis**
4	Covering the lateral aspects of the abdomen is the external oblique.	**External oblique**
5	Deep to the external oblique is the internal oblique.	**Internal oblique**
6	Deep to the internal oblique is the transversus abdominis.	**Transversus abdominis**
7	Superior to the external oblique and attached to the ribs is the serratus anterior	**Serratus anterior**
The external oblique on the left side forms the rectus sheath, which connects to the external oblique on the right side. The rectus sheath envelopes the rectus abdominis muscle.		
The linea alba is the white vertical tissue in the center of the rectus sheath.		
There are tendinous inscriptions subdividing the individual rectus abdominis muscles.		

Table 7B-1   Torso Muscles (continued)

	POSITION DESCRIPTION	MUSCLE
8	On the posterior torso, you will find the upper back muscle that extends across the two shoulders and comes to an inferior point about midway down the back. This is the trapezius.	**Trapezius**
9	Extending from the about the midway area of the trapezius to the lateral sides of the body is the latissimus dorsi.	**Latissimus dorsi**
	Part of the trapezius muscle extends over the shoulder and attaches to the clavicle. You can therefore see a portion of the trapezius on the anterior torso.	
	Part of the latissimus dorsi extends to the humerus so you can see a portion of the latissimus dorsi on the anterior torso.	
	Now, look at the muscles situated between the latissimus dorsi and the trapezius just a bit inferior to the deltoid.	
10	The inferior muscle (immediately superior to the superior edge of the latissimus dorsi) is the teres major.	**Teres major**
11	Superior to the teres major, you can see just a small portion of the teres minor.	**Teres minor**
12	The rest of the muscles in this area appear as a group of three muscles. These make up the infraspinatus muscle.	**Infraspinatus**
13	Deep to the trapezius is the rhomboid major.	**Rhomboid major**
14	Superior to the rhomboid major is the rhomboid minor.	**Rhomboid minor**
	The rotator cuff consists of a group of muscles and their associated tendons that move the shoulder. They are: supraspinatus, infraspinatus, subscapularis, and teres minor. The rotator cuff is not a name for a single muscle.	
15	The supraspinatus is superior to the spine of the scapula and is deep to the trapezius.	**Supraspinatus**
16	The subscapularis is on the anterior surface of the scapula.	**Subscapularis**

Table 7B-2   Deep Torso Muscles

	POSITION DESCRIPTION	MUSCLE
	Deep to the latissimus dorsi and trapezius are groups of muscles that parallel the vertebral column. Collectively, these muscles are called the **erector spinae**.	
1	The muscle nearest the vertebral column is the spinalis thoracis.	**Spinalis thoracis**
2	Lateral to the spinalis thoracis is the longissimus thoracis.	**Longissimus thoracis**
3	Lateral to the longissimus thoracis is the iliocostalis lumborum.	**Iliocostalis lumborum**

PRONUNCIATION

1	Iliocostalis (ill-ee-o-cost-al-is)		5	Rhomboid (rom-boyd)	
2	Latissimus dorsi (luh-tis-i-miss door-see)		6	Spinalis (spy-nal-is)	
3	Longissimus (long-jis-i-mus)		7	Thoracis (thor-aa-sis)	
4	Pectoralis (pek-tor-al-is)		8	Trapezius (truh-pee-zee-us)	

CHAPTER 7C₁   THE TORSO REGION

THE HEART

The heart is a very durable muscular pump. It contracts and relaxes about 68-72 times per minute every day for many years and that's just a passive heart rate (exercise not included). In order to understand how the heart can be such a durable pump, we must learn the anatomy of the heart. The simplest way to learn the anatomy of the heart is to follow a drop of blood in and out of the heart.

The following tables will help you understand the heart parts and to understand the flow of blood through the heart. While studying the following tables, examine the heart models on the lab table along with textbook pictures. When you are finished examining pictures and models, examine the dissected hearts in the lab room.

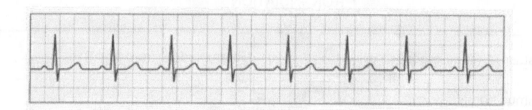

Table 7C$_1$-1   Internal Heart Structures (Flow of Blood)

		Determine the right side of the heart. The wall of the ventricle of the right side is thinner than the wall of the left ventricle.
1	**Right atrium**	Put your finger in the right atrium. This is the location of deoxygenated blood.
2	**Tricuspid valve**	Go through the tricuspid valve.
3	**Right ventricle**	Your finger should now be in the right ventricle.
4	**Pulmonic valve**	Blood is pumped out of the right ventricle through the pulmonic valve into the pulmonary trunk. This is also called the pulmonary valve or pulmonary semilunar valve.
5	**Pulmonary trunk**	The pulmonary trunk ascends and angles a bit to the left.
6	**Pulmonary arteries**	There are 4 pulmonary arteries transporting blood away from the heart toward the lungs (2 to the left lung and 2 to the right lung)
		At the lungs, the blood drops off carbon dioxide and picks up oxygen. The blood is now oxygenated.
7	**Pulmonary veins**	Oxygenated blood is now on its way toward the heart from the lungs. There are 4 pulmonary veins.
8	**Left atrium**	Put your finger in the left atrium of heart.
9	**Bicuspid valve**	Oxygenated blood flows through the bicuspid valve and enters into the left atrium. This valve is also called the mitral valve.
10	**Left ventricle**	Your finger should now be in the left ventricle. Notice the walls of the left ventricle are thicker than the walls of the right ventricle.
11	**Aortic valve**	Blood is pumped out of the left ventricle through the aortic valve and enters the ascending aorta. This is also called the aortic semilunar valve.
12	**Ascending aorta**	The ascending aorta also ascends and angles a bit to the left.

Table 7C$_1$-1   Internal Heart Structures   (Flow of Blood)   (continued)

Some of the blood in the ascending aorta will continue through the aortic arch and some will enter into the coronary vessels. The numbers used in this chart are not referring to the sequence of blood flow.

| 1 | **Coronary vessels** | The right and left coronary arteries branch off the base of the ascending aorta. |
| 2 | **Aortic arch** | The aortic arch arches to the left and posterior to the heart |

The blood in the aortic arch will continue on through the descending aorta but some will branch into the following:

| 3. | **Descending aorta** | The descending aorta is divided into two parts depending on its location in the body: thoracic aorta and abdominal aorta |
| 4 | **Brachiocephalic artery** | This is the first branch off the superior portion of the aortic arch. |

The brachiocephalic artery branches to form the right carotid artery and right subclavian artery.

5	**Right common carotid artery**	Branches off the brachiocephalic artery and goes up the right side of the neck to the brain.
6	**Right subclavian artery**	Branches off the brachiocephalic artery and goes under (sub) the clavicle (clavian) toward the right arm
7	**Left common carotid artery**	This is the second branch off the superior portion of the aortic arch. This goes to the left side of the neck to the brain.
8	**Left subclavian artery**	This goes under (sub) the clavicle (clavian) to the left arm.

Once the oxygenated blood delivers oxygen to all body parts, the blood picks up carbon dioxide and then returns to the heart to eventually go to the lungs so we can exhale the carbon dioxide.

| 1 | **Superior vena cava** | Blood returning from the head region and upper torso enters the SVC to return to the right atrium |
| 2 | **Inferior vena cava** | Blood returning from the lower extremities enters the IVC to return to the right atrium. |

Table 7C₁-2   Other Components of the Internal Heart

		The following structures do not depict the flow of blood through the heart.		
1	**Papillary muscles**	These muscles are located along the walls of the ventricles. They have tendon-like strings attached to them and to the atrio-ventricular valves.
2	**Chordae tendineae**	These tendon-like strings are attached to a valve and to a papillary muscle.
3	**Trabeculae carneae**	These are muscular ridges located in the ventricles. They do not have any chordae tendineae attached to them.
4	**Interventricular septum**	This is the septum that separates the right ventricle from the left ventricle.
5	**Moderator band**	This muscular structure is found only in the right ventricle. You will not see this on the heart models. Be sure to see this on the dissected hearts in the lab room.
6	**Pectinate muscle**	These are muscular ridges found in the atria. Many sources indicate they are only in the right atrium.
7	**Interatrial septum**	This is the septum that separates the right atrium from the left atrium. Sometimes it's not easy to see.

EXERCISE 7C₁-3 EXTERNAL STRUCTURES OF THE HEART

Table 7C₁-3 External Heart Anatomy

There are several ways to determine if you are looking at the anterior side of the heart by looking at an external view.

1	**Anterior interventricular artery**	This artery extends from the coronary vessels at the base of the heart to the apex. This artery angles to the right of the apex of the heart. When you see this, you are looking at the anterior side of the heart.
2	**Posterior interventricular artery**	This artery extends from the coronary vessels at the base of the heart to the apex. This artery goes fairly straight to the apex. When you see this, you are looking at the posterior side of the heart.
3	**Aortic arch**	If the aortic arch is present, it angles to the left of the heart. When you see this, you are looking at the anterior side of the heart.
4	**Pulmonary trunk**	If the pulmonary trunk is present, it angles to the left of the heart. When you see this, you are looking at the anterior side of the heart.
5	**Ligamentum arteriosum** (ductus ligamentum)	This is a ligament-like material that anchors the aortic arch to the pulmonary trunk. This is the remnant of the ductus arteriosum in the fetal heart.

Exercise 7C₁-4   A Dissected Heart

Examine the dissected hearts in the lab room. Your instructor will either show you a few select parts or will have them pinned for identification. In the table below, write the parts that are shown and use the available space to take additional notes.

Table 7C₁-4   The Dissected Heart

	Heart Structure	Notes
1		
2		
3		
4		
5		
6		
7		
8		
9		
10		

PRONUNCIATION

1	Aortic (a-or-tik)		11	Papillary (paa-pi-larry)
2	Ascending (uh-send-ing)		12	Pectinate (pek-ti-nate)
3	Atrium (ay-tree-um)		13	Pulmonary (pul-muh-nare-ee)
4	Bicuspid (bye-cus-pid)		14	Pulmonic (pul-mon-ik)
5	Brachiocephalic (bray-kee-oh-seh-fal-ik)		15	Subclavian (sub-klay-vee-un)
6	Carotid (ku-raw-tid)		16	Superior vena cava (vee-nuh kay-vuh)
7	Chordae tendineae (kor-dee ten-di-nee)		17	Trabeculae carneae (tru-bek-you-lee kar-nee)
8	Coronary (kor-oh-nare-ee)		18	Tricuspid (try-kus-pid)
9	Interventricular (in-ter-ven-trik-you-lar)		19	Ventricle (ven-tri-kul)
10	Ligamentum arteriosum (lig-uh-men-tum ar-teer-ee-oh-sum)			

Chapter 7C₂   The Torso Region

The Blood Vessels

The best way to study the blood vessels is to follow a drop of blood through the vessels.   Begin with a drop of blood in the left ventricle of the heart. Put your finger in the left ventricle. Then, put your finger on each of the vessels listed in sequence using textbook pictures and models in the lab room.

This chapter will concentrate mainly on the blood vessels in the abdomen region and a few in the thoracic region. Begin with a drop of blood in the aortic arch and follow it through the descending aorta, which is made of the thoracic aorta and the abdominal aorta.

EXERCISE 7C$_2$-1   ABDOMINAL ARTERIES

Follow the abdominal aorta until you get to the **celiac trunk** (artery). This artery forms two branches to the left. One is the left **gastric artery** that supplies the lesser curvature of the stomach and the other is the **splenic artery**, which supplies the spleen.

The celiac artery also forms a branch to the right called the **common hepatic artery**. The common hepatic artery eventually supplies the liver and eventually the greater curvature of the stomach.

A few centimeters inferior to the celiac artery is the **superior mesenteric artery**. The superior mesenteric lies over the left renal vein. The superior mesenteric artery supplies:
1. A portion of the jejunum of the small intestine
2. A portion of the ileum of the small intestine
3. Cecum of the large intestine
4. Ascending colon
5. First half of the transverse colon

A few centimeters inferior the superior mesenteric artery is the **inferior mesenteric artery**. This artery is also near the left lateral edge of the abdominal aorta whereas the celiac artery and superior mesenteric artery are in the midline of the abdominal aorta. The inferior mesenteric artery supplies:
1. Second half of the transverse colon
2. Descending colon
3. Sigmoid colon
4. Rectum

Between the superior mesenteric artery and the inferior mesenteric artery are the **gonadal arteries**.

EXERCISE 7C$_2$-2   ABDOMINAL VEINS

The majority of the abdominal veins will enter into the **portal vein**. The portal vein enters into the liver on the inferior side. Once inside the liver, hepatocytes and enzymes will detoxify the blood. Some of the abdominal veins enter into the inferior vena cava.

The venous blood in the liver will enter into **hepatic veins** and then into the inferior vena cava. All of the blood that enters into the inferior vena cava will enter into the right atrium of the heart.

The vessels that go to and from the abdominal organs are embedded in thin membranous material called mesentery.

EXERCISE 7C$_2$-3   THORACIC ARTERIES

Follow blood around the aortic arch into the thoracic aorta. The thoracic aorta and the abdominal aorta make up the descending aorta. The thoracic aorta has several branches the supply the esophagus, bronchial tubes, diaphragm, and intercostal muscles.

Two major arteries to study are the **internal thoracic arteries**, which branch off the left and right subclavian arteries. These arteries supply the internal wall of the chest.

CHAPTER 7D   THE TORSO REGION

THE SPINAL CORD

The spinal cord is part of the central nervous sytem (CNS). The brain is the other part of the CNS. The spinal cord emerges from the brain by passing through the foramen magnum of the skull. The spinal cord passes through the vertebral foramen of the 12 thoracic vertebrae. The final portions of the spinal cord enter into the sacral canal of the sacrum and exits through the sacral hiatus.

There are numerous spinal nerves branching off the spinal cord by passing through foramen. These branches become part of the peripheral nervous the intervertebral system (PNS) since they branch to the periphery of the body.

There are 31 pairs of spinal nerves; 8 pair of cervical nerves, 12 pair of thoracic nerves, 5 pair of lumbar nerves, 5 pair of sacral, and 1 pair of coccygeal nerves.

There are only 7 cervical vertebrae but yet there are 8 cervical nerves.

Reason: The first cervical nerve exits the spinal cord between
vertebra number 1 and the occipital bone of the skull.

Exercise 7D-1 Identification of Spinal Cord Structures

Use your textbook and models to identify the structures listed in table 7D-1.

Using your textbook figures of a transverse view of the spinal cord, identify the parts that are listed in table 10-8. Plus, identify any additional structures listed by your instructor.

Table 7D-1   Spinal Cord and Associated Structures

Conus medullaris
Cauda equina
Filum terminale
Anterior rootlets
Posterior rootlets
Anterior root
Posterior root
Spinal nerve

EXERCISE 7D-2   TRANSVERSE VIEW OF THE SPINAL CORD

A dissecting microscope is set up for you to view the following structures listed in table 7D-2.

Table 7D-2   Transverse View of the Spinal Cord

Central canal	Anterior white column
Posterior sulcus	Lateral white column
Anterior sulcus	Posterior white column
Gray matter	Anterior gray
White matter	Lateral gray
	Posterior gray

CHAPTER 7E   THE TORSO REGION

THE LUNGS

The respiratory system consists of more than just the lungs for the exchange of carbon dioxide for oxygen. It also consists of numerous structures that are designed to protect the respiratory process.

The respiratory structures associated with the nasal cavity and the oral cavity is considered to be the upper respiratory structures. The trachea, bronchi and lungs are considered to be the lower respiratory structures.

At your lab table is a model showing the sagittal view of the head. You will use this view to help you study the upper respiratory structures of the head and neck region. You will then use manikins to study the respiratory structures of the lower respiratory structures of the thoracic cavity. Follow the information listed in tables 7E-1 through 7E-4 while examining the sagittal view of the head. Use the manikin torso to study tables 7E-5 through 7E-7.

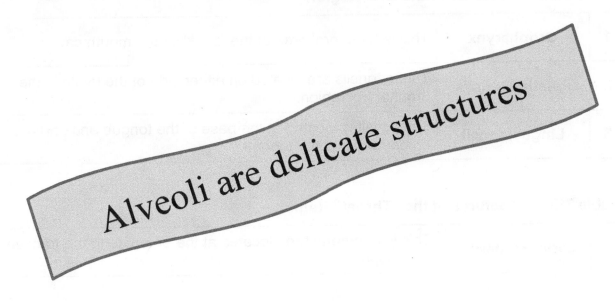

Alveoli are delicate structures

Table 7E-1   Features of the Nasal Cavity

1	**External nares**	These are the openings into the nasal cavity.
2	**Nasal conchae**	These are the bulges on the inside lining of the nasal cavity
	The nasal conchae will cause the inhaled air to become turbulent, thereby warming the air as it moves into the trachea. The nasal conchae are also covered with mucus to "trap" any inhaled debris thereby preventing the debris from going into the lungs.	
3	**Nasopharynx**	This is a general area at the "back" of the nasal cavity
4	**Pharyngeal tonsil**	These tonsils are located in superior part of the nasopharynx region. In layman's terms, these are the adenoids.

Table 7E-2   Features of the Oral Region

1	**Oropharynx**	This is a general area at the "back" of the mouth cavity.
2	**Palatine tonsils**	These tonsils are located on either side of the uvula in the oropharynx region.
3	**Lingual tonsil**	This tonsil is located at the base of the tongue and partially embedded into the tongue.

Table 7E-3   Features of the "Throat" Region

1	**Laryngopharynx**	This is a general area located at the entrance to the trachea and the esophagus.

Table 7E-4   Features of the Trachea

1	Thyroid cartilage	This is a rather large piece of cartilage that has a prominent anterior bulge.
2	Laryngeal prominence	This is the anterior bulge on the thyroid cartilage. In layman's terms it is the "Adam's apple." This is also called the thyroid prominence.
3	Cricoid cartilage	This is the second largest piece of cartilage on the trachea. It is inferior to the thyroid cartilage.
4	Tracheal cartilage	These are the cartilaginous rings around the trachea. These rings are not complete rings. They only wrap ¾ of the way around the trachea.
5	Trachea	The trachea is a tube with a rather large diameter located anterior to the esophagus.
6	Glottis	This is the entrance to the trachea.
7	Epiglottis	This is a piece of cartilage located over the trachea, which functions to close off the trachea upon swallowing of food to prevent choking.
8	Trachealis muscle	This is the muscle tissue that makes up the posterior side of the cartilage rings of the trachea.
9	Carina	This is a ridge at the lower end of the trachea that separates the openings of the left and right bronchi.
10	Left and Right bronchi	These are the respiratory tubes that branch off the trachea thus entering into the lungs. They are called the primary bronchi.
11	Hilum	This is the "indentation" of each lung where the primary bronchi enter the lung.
12	Intrapulmonary bronchi	These are the branches of the bronchi inside the lungs

Table 7E-5   Features of the Bronchi and Lungs

1	**Right lung**	Consists of 3 lobes.

The right primary bronchus branches to form 3 secondary bronchi (one per lobe). The secondary bronchi branch to form a total of 10 tertiary bronchi going to 10 lung segments.

2	**Left lung**	Consists of 2 lobes.

The left primary bronchus branches to form 2 secondary bronchi (one per lobe). The secondary bronchi branch to form a total of 9 tertiary bronchi going to 9 lung segments.

3	**Cartilage**	The trachea and primary bronchi have cartilage rings. The secondary and tertiary bronchi have cartilage plates. These are designed to prevent respiratory tube collapse.
4	**Bronchioles**	Bronchioles do not have any cartilage for support. Due to the small diameter of the bronchioles, they are self-supporting.
5	**Alveoli**	The bronchioles terminate with small air sacs called alveoli.

Alveoli are surrounded by capillaries. This is the place where gas exchange occurs. Oxygen leaves the alveolus and enters the circulatory system. Carbon dioxide leaves the circulatory system and enters the alveolus to be exhaled.

EXERCISE 7E-3   ADDTIONAL STRUCTURES OF THE LUNGS

Table 7E-6   More Lung Information

1	Apex	This is the superior part of the lung (the "pointy" end).
2	Base	This is the inferior part of the lung nearest the diaphragm muscle.
3	Costal surface	This is the surface of lung tissue adjacent to the thoracic wall.
4	Mediastinal surface	This is the medial side of each lung nearest the mediastinum (sternum area).
5	Diaphragmatic surface	This is the surface of the lung adjacent to the diaphragm muscle.
6	Cardiac notch	This is the concave notch (for the apex of the heart) located in the left lung on the medial surface.

Table 7E-7   Respiratory Muscles

1	Diaphragm muscle	In order to inhale, this muscle depresses (contracts). This will increase the size of the thoracic cavity. In order to exhale, this muscle elevates (relaxes). This will decrease the size of the thoracic cavity.
2	External intercostal	These muscles will elevate the ribs. This will increase the size of the thoracic cavity. Inhalation occurs.
3	Internal intercostal	These muscles will depress the ribs. This will decrease the size of the thoracic cavity. Exhalation occurs.

There are other muscles that assist in respiration but the above are the major muscles involved in breathing.
The external intercostal muscles angle from the inferior rib to the superior rib posteriorly.
The internal intercostal muscles angle from the inferior rib to the superior rib anteriorly.

PRONUNCIATION

1	Alveoli (al-vee-oh-lye)		11	Hilum (high-lum)
2	Bronchi (brong-ki)		12	Intrapulmonary (in-truh-pull-moe-nary)
3	Bronchiole (brong-kee-ohl)		13	Laryngeal (lare-in-jee-ul)
4	Carina (kuh-rye-nuh)		14	Laryngopharynx (lare-ing-oh-fare-inks)
5	Conchae (kong-kee)		15	Mediastinal (mee-dee-uh-sty-nul)
6	Costal (kos-tul)		16	Nares (nare-z)
7	Cricoid (kry-koyd)		17	Nasopharynx (nay-zoe-fare-inks)
8	Diaphragm (die-uh-fram)		18	Oropharynx (or-oh-fare-inks)
9	Diaphragmatic (die-uh-frag-maa-tik)		19	Trachea (tray-kee-uh)
10	Epiglottis (eh-pi-glaw-tis)			

CHAPTER 7F   THE TORSO REGION

THE ABDOMINAL ORGANS

The main function of the digestive system is to break down large molecules into smaller molecules that can be used by the cells of body. The organs that are directly involved in digestion are the oral cavity, stomach, and small intestine. However, there are several organs that are indirectly involved in the digestive process. Organs such as the pancreas, liver, and gallbladder are indirectly involved.

Food enters the **oral cavity** and is masticated by the **teeth**. The **salivary glands** produce *salivary amylase*. Salivary amylase will begin to digest carbohydrates. The **tongue** will push the partially digested food to the back of the mouth where it will be swallowed into the **esophagus**. The peristaltic action of the esophagus will force food (bolus) toward the **stomach**. The esophagus passes from the thoracic cavity to the abdominal cavity by going through an opening in the diaphragm muscle called the esophageal hiatus.

Food enters the stomach by passing through the **esophageal sphincter**. Food continues into the **body** of the stomach. The food will continue to be digested as the stomach cells produce *pepsinogen* and *hydrochloric acid*. The combination of those two chemicals will produce the digestive enzyme *pepsin*. Pepsin will partially digest protein. This partially digested food is now called acidic chyme. This acidic chyme enters the **pyloris** area of the stomach and then through the **pyloric sphincter** into the **duodenum** of the **small intestine**.

The small intestine is made of three regions, the **duodenum, jejunum,** and **ileum**. The small intestine contains digestive enzymes too. It contains *peptidase*, which will digest protein. It contains *lactase*, which will digest some carbohydrates (lactose).

The **pancreas** releases numerous digestive enzymes that will assist in the digestion of food. *Pancreatic amylase* from the pancreas will enter into the duodenum of the small intestine and will digest carbohydrates. *Trypsin* from the pancreas will enter into the duodenum of the small intestine and will digest protein. *Lipase* from the pancreas will enter the duodenum of the small intestine and will digest fat. As you can see, there is actually far more digestion occurring in the small intestine as compared to the stomach. (In a physiology class, you will learn that the stomach has other functions than digestion). Food passes through the small intestine via peristaltic action.

The **liver** produces *bile*. Bile will enter and is stored in the **gallbladder**. From either the liver or the gallbladder, bile will exit and enter into the duodenum of the small intestine and emulsify the fat that is in the small intestine. This emulsification process helps lipase to be more efficient at digesting fat.

The small molecules that are produced via the digestive process are now called nutrients. These nutrients are absorbed into the bloodstream via structures called **villi**. The blood will transport these nutrients to all cells of the body.

Any food substance that has not been digested and absorbed by the time it reaches the **large intestine**, it is considered to be waste. These waste products will pass through the **ileocecal valve** leading to the **cecum**, which is the first part of the large intestine. Due to the peristaltic activity of the muscles of the large intestine, waste products will pass through the **ascending colon**, then to through the **transverse colon**, then through the **descending colon**. The waste product then passes through the last portion of the large intestine called the **sigmoid colon** and the **rectum**. The muscles involved in the peristaltic action of the large intestine are the **taeneia coli** and the **haustra**.

There is a tremendous amount of water that passes through the digestive system with every meal. We cannot afford to lose very much water at all. The large intestine not only functions to get rid of waste products but it also prevents dehydration. Much of the water that enters into the large intestine will be reabsorbed by the large intestine into the bloodstream.

EXERCISE 7F-1   IDENTIFICATION OF THE DIGESTIVE STRUCTURES

At your lab table is a model showing the sagittal view of the head. You will use this view to help you study the digestive structures of the head and neck region. You will then use manikins to study the digestive structures of the abdominal cavity.

Table 7F-1   The Path of Food Through the Mouth and Esophagus

1	**Teeth**	Incisors and cuspids are used for tearing food. Bicuspids and molars are used for grinding food.
2	**Tongue**	This huge muscular structure pushes the food to the back of the throat for swallowing.
3	**Oropharynx**	This is the area of the pharynx at the back of the mouth.
4	**Uvula**	Posterior to the tongue in the oropharynx region is a "hangy-down" thing.
5	**Epiglottis**	This is a piece of cartilage that acts as a "flap" to close of the tracheal opening when a person is swallowing food.
	The action by the epiglottis will ensure that food will go down the esophagus and not the trachea.	
6	**Esophagus**	This is the "food tube" that is posterior to the trachea.
	By the muscular action of the esophagus, food will descend the esophagus and enter into the stomach. This muscular action is called **peristalsis**.	
7	**Parotid gland**	Turn the model over and you will find posterior to the masseter muscle a large salivary gland called the parotid gland.
8	**Submandibular gland**	This is the salivary gland located within the mandible area.
9	**Sublingual gland**	This is the salivary gland located under the tongue.

Use manikins to study the digestive structures of the abdominal cavity. Follow the information listed in table 7F-2 while examining the abdominal region of the manikin.

Table 7F-2   Digestive Structures of the Abdominal Region (manikin)

		The esophagus descends the thoracic cavity and passes through the diaphragm muscle. Then, the esophagus bends a bit to the left to connect to the stomach.
1	**Stomach**	The stomach is located a bit to the left of the midline of the body.
2	**Duodenum**	Food leaves the stomach and enters into the first part of the small intestine called the duodenum.
3	**Jejunum**	Food continues on through the second part of the small intestine called the jejunum.
4	**Ileum**	Food continues on through the ileum, the last part of the small intestine.
5	**Cecum**	This is the first part of the large intestine. Digestion is complete. The material is now referred to as waste.
6	**Ascending colon**	Waste travels through the ascending colon, which is on the right side of the abdomen.
7	**Transverse colon**	Waste travels through the ascending colon, which traverses across the abdomen, inferior to the diaphragm muscle.
8	**Descending colon**	Waste travels through the descending colon, which is on the left side of the abdomen.
9	**Sigmoid colon**	Waste travels toward the rectum by traveling through the sigmoid colon, which curves to the right toward the rectum from the descending colon.
10	**Rectum**	The rectum leads from the sigmoid colon to the anus.

Tables 7F-3 through 7F-9 describe special features of the various organs involved in digestion.

Table 7F-3   Features of the Stomach

1	**Cardia**	This is the area of the joining of the esophagus to the stomach.
2	**Esophageal sphincter**	This is the lower sphincter of the esophagus that opens to allow food to enter the stomach.
3	**Fundus**	This is the large rounded portion of the stomach. This region is nearest the spleen.
4	**Body**	The body of the stomach is the main portion involved in digestion.
5	**Gastric rugae**	These are the muscular folds inside the body of the stomach.
6	**Pylorus**	This is the last part of the stomach, which connects to the duodenum of the small intestine.
7	**Pyloric sphincter**	This sphincter opens to allow food to enter into the duodenum.
8	**Greater curvature**	This is the inferior, convex curve of the stomach.
9	**Lesser curvature**	This is the superior, concave curve of the stomach.
10	**Muscles of the stomach**	Circular muscles Longitudinal muscles Oblique muscles

Table 7F-4   Features of the Small Intestine

1	**Duodenum**	This is the first part of the small intestine. It is about ten inches in length. Numerous digestive enzymes enter the duodenum from the pancreas.
2	**Hepatopancreatic sphincter**	This sphincter opens thus allowing digestive enzymes from the pancreas to enter the duodenum. This sphincter opens thus allowing bile from the liver and gallbladder to enter the duodenum.
3	**Jejunum**	The jejunum is about eight feet in length. Most of the digestion and absorption occurs in the jejunum.
4	**Intestinal villi**	Lining most of the small intestine are intestinal villi. Villi will absorb the nutrients thus allowing nutrients to enter into the bloodstream and then travel to all parts of the body.
5	**Ileum**	This is the last part of the small intestine. It is approximately twelve feet in length. The ileum connects to the cecum of the large intestine.
6	**Ileocecal valve**	This valve opens to allow material to enter the cecum from the ileum.

The large intestine does not digest for nor does it absorb nutrients. Its function is:

1. Reabsorb water into the bloodstream to prevent dehydration
2. House bacteria that are involved in making vitamin K, which is necessary to make some blood clotting factors.
3. Propel waste to the anal region.

Table 7F-5   Features of the Large Intestine

1	**Cecum**	The appendix is attached to the cecum.
2	**Haustra**	These are numerous folds within the large intestine that allows for distention
3	**Taeniae coli**	This is a ribbon of smooth muscle that extends the length of the large intestine. This muscle provides peristaltic action of the large intestine. There are three sets of taeniae coli. One set is associated with each part of the large intestine (ascending, transverse, and descending colon).
4	**Hepatic flexure**	This is the bend of the large intestine from the ascending colon to the transverse colon. Also called the right colic flexure.
5	**Splenic flexure**	This is the bend of the large intestine from the transverse colon to the descending colon. Also called the left colic flexure.
6	**Sigmoid flexure**	This is the bend of the large intestine from the descending colon to the sigmoid colon.

Table 7F-6   Features of the Abdominal Region

1	**Mesentery proper**	This is the thin membranous material found between the folds of the small intestine. Embedded in this membrane are blood vessels that are involved in absorbing nutrients from the small intestine.
2	**Greater omentum**	This is the mesentery that extends from the greater curvature of the stomach and drapes over the intestines like an apron. It is thicker than the mesentery proper.
3	**Lesser omentum**	This is the mesentery that extends from the lesser curvature of the stomach to the liver.

EXERCISE 7F-2 IDENTIFICATION OF THE ACCESSORY STRUCTURES OF DIGESTION

The liver, gallbladder, and pancreas are considered accessory organs of digestion. These organs do not digest food directly but they produce products that are involved in the process. The liver produces bile and the gallbladder stores bile. The pancreas produces numerous enzymes. All of these products (bile and pancreatic enzymes) enter the duodenum by passing through the hepatopancreatic sphincter.

Table 7F-7   Features of the Liver

The liver is the largest abdominal organ of the body. It has numerous functions in addition to being involved in the digestive processes.		
1	**Right lobe and Left lobe**	The liver is made of several lobes of which these two you can easily see from an anterior view.
2	**Falciform ligament**	This is mesentery type tissue that marks the boundary between the right and left lobe of the liver.
3	**Coronary ligament**	As the falciform ligament ascends between the lobes, it divides and spreads across the top of the liver, just inferior to the diaphragm muscle.
4	**Hepatocytes**	Cells of the liver that produce bile.
5	**Left and Right Hepatic ducts**	Bile flows from the hepatocytes into these hepatic ducts.
6	**Common hepatic duct**	Bile flows from the hepatic ducts into the common hepatic duct.
7	**Common bile duct**	Bile continues on through the common bile duct.
8	**Duodenum**	The hepatopancreatic sphincter opens to allow bile to enter into the duodenum.
Bile does not digest anything. Bile will emulsify fat, which makes it easier for lipase to do its job. Lipase is the enzyme that does the digestion of fat.		

Table 7F-8   Features of the Gallbladder

The gallbladder will store 40 to 70 mL of bile. The gallbladder does not make bile but it will concentrate the bile it is storing.		
1	**Cystic duct**	Bile flows out of the gallbladder into the cystic duct.
2	**Common bile duct**	Bile flows into the common bile duct.
3	**Duodenum**	The hepatopancreatic sphincter opens to allow bile to enter into the duodenum.
Listed below is the process involved in getting bile from the liver into the gallbladder for storage.		
<ul><li>The hepatopancreatic sphincter is closed.</li><li>Bile "back flows" into the common bile duct.</li><li>Bile "back flows" into the cystic duct.</li><li>Bile enters into the gallbladder</li></ul>		

The pancreas produces numerous enzymes that enter into the duodenum to mix with the enzymes already produced by the small intestine cells.

Table 7F-9   Features of the Pancreas

		The pancreas consists of cells that produce hormones (endocrine cells) and cells that produce enzymes (exocrine cells).	
1	**Pancreatic lobules**	The lobules consist of cells that produce enzymes for digestion.
2	**Pancreatic islets**	The islets are clusters of cells within the lobules that produce the hormones, such as insulin.
3	**Pancreatic duct**	Enzymes travel through the pancreatic duct to enter into the duodenum after passing through the hepatopancreatic sphincter.

Table 7F-10   Other Features of the Liver, Gallbladder, and Pancreas

1	**Fundus of liver**	This is the large rounded portion of the liver on the superior, right side.
2	**Fundus of the gallbladder**	This is the rounded, inferior portion of the gallbladder.
3	**Pancreatic head**	The head of the pancreas is adjacent to the duodenum.
4	**Pancreatic tail**	The tail of the pancreas is the narrow portion that is nearest the spleen.
5	**Pancreatic body**	The main portion of the pancreas between the head and the tail.

PRONUNCIATION

1	Ascending (uh-send-ing)	16	Gastric rugae (gas-rik roo-gee)
2	Body (baw-dee)	17	Haustra (haws-truh)
3	Cardia (kar-dee-uh)	18	Hepatic (heh-paa-tik)
4	Cecum (see-kum)	19	Hepatocytes (heh-paa-toe-sites)
5	Colon (kole-un)	20	Hepatopancreatic (heh-paa-toe-pan-kree-aa-tik)
6	Coronary (kore-uh-nare-ee)	21	Ileocecal (ill-lee-oh-see-kul)
7	Cystic (sis-tik)	22	Ileum (ill-lee-um)
8	Descending (dee-sen-ding)	23	Jejunum (juh-joo-num)
9	Duodenum (doo-oh-dee-num)	24	Mesentery (mez-en-tare-ee)
10	Epiglottis (eh-pi-glaw-tis)	25	Omentum (oh-men-tum)
11	Esophageal sphincter (ee-sof-uh-jee-ul sfink-ter)	26	Oropharynx (or-oh-fare-inks)
12	Esophagus (ee-sof-uh-gus)	27	Parotid (puh-raw-tid)
13	Falciform (fal-si-form)	28	Pyloric (pie-lor-ik)
14	Flexure (flex-er)	29	Pylorus (pie-lor-us)
15	Fundus (fun-dus)	30	Sigmoid (sig-moyd)

31	Sphincter (sfink-ter)	35	Submandibular (sub-man-dib-you-lar)
32	Splenic (spee-nik)	36	Taeniae coli (tee-nee-uh koe-lee)
33	Stomach (stum-ik)	37	Transverse (trans-vers)
34	Sublingual (sub-ling-you-ul)	38	Uvula (you-view-luh)

CHAPTER 8   THE PELVIC REGION

Chapter 8 discusses the structures associated with the pelvic region. Chapter 8 is divided into different sections as indicated below:

8A: The urinary system

8B: The male reproductive system

8C: The female reproductive system

The material used in this lab will be (but not limited to):

Models of the kidney showing blood vessels and nephron

Dissected sheep kidneys

Male reproductive models

Female reproductive models

Models that show broad ligaments, etc.

Models that show different stages of pregnancy

Human uterus

CHAPTER 8A   THE PELVIC REGION

THE URINARY SYSTEM

As the body operates daily, it produces waste products from the metabolism of nutrients. The waste products must be eliminated from the body in order for the body to continue functioning properly. There are many ways to get rid of metabolic wastes. The respiratory system gets rid of carbon dioxide. The integumentary system aids in getting rid of products via sweat. The digestive system is responsible for eliminating solid waste material (feces). The urinary system is responsible for getting rid of liquid waste, primarily nitrogenous waste. You will learn in a physiology class that the kidneys do more than just get rid of liquid wastes. The kidneys produce some hormones, they are involved in red blood cell formation, they help regulate body fluid pH, and the list continues. In this course, we concentrate on the anatomical structures involved in the elimination of waste products.

In general, the waste products produced by cellular metabolism can be found in the bloodstream. The blood enters the kidneys via the **renal arteries**. This blood enters the **interlobar arterioles**. From there it continues into the **arcuate arterioles**. The arcuate arterioles then branch into the **interlobular arterioles**. Blood from the interlobular arterioles will enter into the **afferent arteriole** and then into the **glomerular capillaries**, which are inside the **glomerular capsule**.

Waste products will then leave the glomerular capillaries and enter into the first part of the *nephron* called the **glomerular capsule**. The waste products will continue into the **proximal convoluted tubule**, then to the **nephron loop**, then to the **distal convoluted tubule**, then into the **collecting duct**. The collecting duct collects waste products from several nephrons at a time (hence the name, collecting duct).

Several collecting ducts will travel through the **renal pyramid** area of the kidneys. The collecting ducts will "dump" their waste products together in area called the **minor calyx**. Several minor calyces will join together to form the **major calyx**. Several major calyces will join together to form the **renal pelvis**. The waste products in the renal pelvis will continue into the **ureter**.

Each kidney has one ureter and each ureter will "dump" the waste products into the **urinary bladder**. When the urinary bladder contracts to eliminate the liquid waste, the *internal urethral sphincter* opens to let the urine out of the urinary bladder and into the **urethra**. A few centimeters inferior to the internal urethral sphincter is the **external urethral sphincter**. When this last sphincter opens, well you guessed it; you better hope that you are in an appropriate place.

The blood that carried waste products to the glomerular capillaries does not enter into the glomerular capsule. If it does, you would have blood in the urine. Therefore, under normal circumstances, the blood exits the glomerular capillaries and enters into the **efferent arteriole**. The efferent arteriole will lead to the **vasa recta**. The vasa recta then forms the **interlobular venules**, then the **arcuate venules**, then the **interlobar venules**. From the interlobar venules, the blood enters the **renal vein**. The renal vein will then carry the blood to the **inferior vena cava**, which then takes the blood back to the **right atrium**. Since the blood "dropped off" the waste products at the glomerular capsule, the blood entering the efferent arteriole is actually "cleaner" than the blood that was in the afferent arteriole. In this sense, the kidneys act as a filter.

There is a tremendous amount of water that enters the kidneys on a daily basis. It has been estimated that about 50 gallons enter both kidneys every 24 hours. That is too much water to be losing! We would dehydrate if we lost that much water. We would have to literally drink 50 gallons of water per day to replace the amount that was lost. We would have to drink about 33 glasses of water every hour. Wow! Fortunately, our kidneys do not excrete all of the water that enters it. Much of the water present in the nephron (proximal convoluted tubule, nephron loop, and the distal convoluted tubule) and the collecting duct will reenter the bloodstream by entering into the vasa recta. In fact, over 99% of the water that entered into the glomerular capsule will return to the bloodstream. Therefore, a glass of water every 2 hours or so is sufficient.

Table 8A-1   Sagittal View of the Kidney

The sagittal view of the kidney shows three distinct regions. The regions are listed below.		
1	**Renal cortex**	This is the "outer" region of the sagittal kidney.
2	**Renal medulla**	This is the "inner" area of the sagittal kidney
3	**Renal pelvis**	This is the "funnel" portion of the kidney that extends from the renal medulla to the ureter.
4	**Renal pyramids**	These are pyramidal-shaped structures comprising the renal medulla region.
5	**Renal columns**	These are areas found between each renal pyramid.
6	**Collecting ducts**	Many times you will see "stripes" within the renal pyramids. These are tubes that extend from the nephrons that lead to the calyces.
7	**Minor calyx**	Each renal pyramid transports urine to a minor calyx.
8	**Major calyx**	Several minor calyces merge to form a major calyx.
9	**Ureter**	Several major calyces merge to form the ureter.
10	**Hilum**	This is the concave portion of the kidney on its medial side. The ureter and renal vein exits the hilum while the renal artery enters the hilum area.

Table 8A-2   The Nephron

The nephron is considered to be the functional unit of the kidneys. The nephron "processes" the waste thereby forming the urine that exits the body.		
There are two major types of nephrons. They are named according to their location in the kidney. There are about 800,000 to 1.5 million nephrons in each kidney		
1	**Cortical nephron**	Most of this nephron is located mainly in the cortex region of the kidney. 85% of the nephrons are cortical nephrons.
2	**Juxtamedullary nephron**	Most of this nephron is located nearest the medulla region of the kidney.
3	**Glomerular capsule**	This is the first part of the nephron. An old term for this structure is renal corpuscle.
4	**PCT**	The proximal convoluted tubule is the second part of the nephron.
5	**Nephron loop**	This is the third part of the nephron. This used to be called the "loop of Henle" but Henle is a person's name so anatomists are doing away with that term.
The nephron loop consists of the descending limb, loop, and ascending limb		
6	**DCT**	The distal convoluted tubule is the fourth part of the nephron.
7	**Collecting duct**	The collecting duct is not a part of any particular nephron. The DCT of several nephrons merge to a single collecting duct.
Numerous collecting ducts merge to form a minor calyx.		

EXERCISE 8A-3   IDENTIFICATION OF BLOOD VESSELS

Table 8A-3   The Blood Vessels of the Kidneys

Waste products need to be transported to the kidneys to be excreted.		
The list below begins with waste in the descending aorta and leads to the nephron. At the nephron, the waste is "dropped off" and the "cleaner" blood returns to the inferior vena cava.		
1	**Descending aorta**	Waste products leave the cells and enter into the circulatory system. The blood travels to the heart and then eventually leaves the heart and enters the descending aorta.
2	**Renal artery**	The renal arteries branch off the descending aorta and enters into the kidneys.
3	**Segmental artery**	Once inside the kidney, the renal artery branches to form segmental arteries.
4	**Interlobar artery**	The interlobar arteries "travel" toward the cortex via the renal columns.
5	**Arcuate artery**	The arcuate arteries "run along" the border of the renal medulla and renal cortex
6	**Interlobular artery**	Current research is suggesting changing the name to cortical radiate arteries. These arteries extend into the cortex region.
7	**Afferent arteriole**	These are small arterioles that branch off the interlobular arteries and enter into the glomerular capsule.
8	**Glomerular capillaries**	These are capillaries that are inside the glomerular capsule.
Waste products leave the capillaries through openings called **fenestrae (fenestrated openings)**. Waste then enters the capsular space on its way to the PCT.		

Table 8A-3 The Blood Vessels of the Kidneys (continued)

Waste products leave the glomerular capillaries and enter into the PCT.		
The capillaries leaving the glomerular capsule consist of blood that is "cleaner" than the blood that entered the capsule. This "clean" blood is on its way to the inferior vena cava.		
1	**Glomerular capillaries**	These are the capillaries inside the glomerular capsule.
2	**Efferent arteriole**	This arteriole exits the capsule.
3	**Peritubular capillaries**	These capillaries intertwine in and around the PCT and DCT area. The peritubular capillaries will continue to intertwine with the nephron loop associated with the cortical nephrons.
The peritubular capillaries will form **vasa recta** if it's associated with the juxtamedullary nephrons.		
4	**Interlobular veins**	The peritubular capillaries and/ or the vasa recta will form the interlobular veins.
5	**Arcuate veins**	These veins "run along" the border of the renal cortex and renal medulla.
6	**Interlobar veins**	These veins traverse along the renal columns.
7	**Renal vein**	The renal vein transports "cleaner" blood to the inferior vena cava.

Table 8A-4   The Ureters, Urinary Bladder, and Urethra

1	Ureter	The ureter exits the kidney at the hilum area
2	Ureteral opening	The ureters enter the urinary bladder on the posterior, inferior aspect of the urinary bladder.
3	Vesicourethral valve	The ureteral openings are slit-like openings. As the urinary bladder relaxes, the slit-like openings expand, thus allowing urine to enter. This is not a true valve. Therefore, many researchers are suggesting to refer to this action of opening as a vesicourethral valve mechanism.
	When the urinary bladder tenses, the slit-like openings squeeze shut thereby preventing urine from entering into the ureters in a "back-flow" manner.	
4	Internal urethral sphincter	In order for urine to leave the urinary bladder, the internal urethral sphincter must open.
	This sphincter consists of smooth muscle and is therefore under involuntary control.	
5	Urethra	There is a single tube that exits the urinary bladder.
6	External urethral sphincter	Toward the distal end of the urethra (about 2cm from the internal urethral sphincter) there is the external urethral sphincter.
	This sphincter consists of skeletal muscle and is therefore under conscious control. This is the sphincter that we learned to control during our days of potty training.	
7	Detrusor muscles	These are the muscles that comprise the urinary bladder
8	Trigone	Inside the urinary bladder is a smooth, triangular area. This area is bordered by the two ureteral openings and the urethral opening. It aids in "funneling" urine toward the urethra.

PRONUNCIATION

1	Afferent (aff-er-ent)	10	Interlobular (in-ter-law-byou-lar)
2	Arcuate (are-kew-ate)	11	Juxtamedullary (juks-tuh-med-you-lary)
3	Calyx (kay-liks))	12	Peritubular (pare-i-too-byou-lar)
4	Detrusor (dee-troo-ser)	13	Segmental (seg-men-tul)
5	Efferent (eff-er-ent)	14	Trigone (try-goen)
6	Fenestrae (fen-eh-stray)	15	Ureter (yer-eh-ter)
7	Glomerular (glow-mare-you-lar)	16	Urethra (you-ree-thruh)
8	Hilum (high-lum)	17	Urethral (you-ree-thrul)
9	Interlobar (in-ter-low-bar)	18	Vesicourethral (ves-i-koe-you-ree-thrul)

CHAPTER 8B   THE PELVIC REGION

THE MALE REPRODUCTIVE SYSTEM

The reproductive system is quite unique from the other systems of the body. The other systems of the body function to support the survival of the individual organism. The reproductive system is not needed for the survival of the organism but rather is needed to perpetuate the species. Not only do the other organ systems function for the survival of the organism but they also function to ensure the reproductive system operates in such a manner that the end result is the production of an offspring.

In a sense, the main function of the male reproductive system is to produce viable sperm cells. The main function of the female reproductive system is to provide a viable egg and act as a receptacle for the sperm cells. The female reproductive system also functions to provide nourishment for the developing child.

There are numerous changes that take place in the female's body during pregnancy. During pregnancy the woman experiences a few bouts of constipation and a relative constant urge to urinate. During pregnancy, the woman also experiences difficulty in breathing. After studying the female reproductive anatomy, you will begin to understand why the woman experiences some of these conditions.

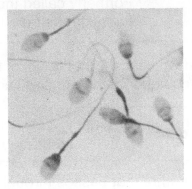

EXERCISE 8B-1   THE PASSAGE OF SPERM CELLS

At your lab table is a model of the male and female reproductive system. You are to follow the path of sperm cells as they travel through the reproductive system and follow the path of an egg as it travels through the reproductive system.

Table 8B-1   The Pathway of Sperm Cells

	Reproductive structure	Description of the location
1	**Seminiferous tubules**	These tubules are inside the testes.
2	**Straight tubules**	The seminiferous tubules form numerous straight tubules that form a mesh of tubes collectively called the **rete testis**.
3	**Efferent ductules**	Tubules that connect the rete testis to the epididymis.
4	**Epididymis**	This is a series of coiled tubes located on the posterior edge of the testis.
	The epididymis consists of the head, body, and the tail. The tail is at the inferior edge of the testis.	
5	**Ductus deferens**	Formerly called the vas deferens. This is an uncoiled tube that extends from the tail of the epididymis.
	The ductus deferens ascends from the tail of the epididymis and loops around the ureter and passes posterior to the urinary bladder and leads to the ejaculatory duct.	
6	**Ejaculatory duct**	This duct passes through the prostate gland and merges with the urethra coming from the urinary bladder.
	The portion of the urethra that passes through the prostate gland is called the **prostatic urethra**.	
7	**Penile urethra**	Sperm cells flow through the penile urethra to exit the male's body.

EXERCISE 8B-2   THE ACCESSORY GLANDS

Table 8B-2   Accessory Glands of the Male Reproductive System

	Reproductive structure	Description of the location
1	**Seminal vesicle gland**	The tube from this gland merges with the ejaculatory duct.
2	**Prostate gland**	The prostate gland is located inferior to the urinary bladder.
3	**Bulbo-urethral gland**	The tube from this gland merges with the penile urethral just slightly inferior to the prostate gland

The seminal vesicle gland produces 60% of the volume of semen. Consists of a high concentration of fructose (nutrients for sperm cells).
The prostate gland produces 20-30% of the volume of semen.
The bulbo-urethral gland produces a thick alkaline mucus. This mucus provides lubrication at the tip end of the penis.

EXERCISE 8B-3   IDENTIFICATION OF PENIS AND SCROTUM STRUCTURES

The penis consists of three cylindrical erectile tissues. The testes are housed in the scrotum.

Table 8B-3   The Anatomy of the Penis and Scrotum

	Reproductive structure	Description of the location
1	**Corpora cavernosa**	A pair of cylindrical tissues that are parallel to each other and extend from the posterior edge of the glans to the crus of the penis, which are attached to the ramus of the ischium. In the center of each corpora cavernosa is an artery.
2	**Corpus spongiosum**	This single cylindrical tissue lies under the corpora cavernosa. It surrounds the penile urethra.
3	**Root of the penis**	The root of the penis attaches to the ramus of the ischium
4	**Shaft of the penis**	The shaft consists of the corpora cavernosa and spongiosum. These are the erectile tissues of the penis.
5	**Glans**	This is expanded tissue at the distal end of the penis. It surrounds the external urethral orifice.
6	**Scrotum**	The scrotum is divided into two chambers and houses the testes.
7	**Perineal raphe**	Thickened scrotal tissue that lies along the scrotal partition. It extends from the anus and along the anterior surface of the penis.
8	**Dartos muscle**	Smooth muscle in the dermis of the scrotum. Creates the characteristic wrinkling of the scrotal surface.
9	**Cremaster muscle**	Muscles that pull the testes closer to the body in an effort to maintain warm temperature (cremasteric reflex).

CHAPTER 8C   THE PELVIC REGION

THE FEMALE REPRODUCTIVE SYSTEM

Table 8C-1 lists the pathway of an unfertilized egg. Table 8C-2 lists the pathway of a fertilized egg.

Table 8C-1   The Pathway of an Unfertilized Egg

	Reproductive structure	Description of the location
1	Ovary	The ovaries are located lateral to the superior portion of the uterus.
2	Uterine tube	The tubes extend from the ovaries to the body of the uterus in the fundus area.
		The **fimbriae** move in such a manner to "draw" the ovulated egg into the opening of the uterine tube. Once inside the uterine tube, the egg continues to move via cilia that line the uterine tube.
		If the egg is not fertilized within 48 hours after ovulation, it will begin to decompose.

Table 8C-2   The Pathway of a Fertilized Egg

	Reproductive structure	Description of the location
1	Ovary	The ovaries are located lateral to the superior portion of the uterus.
2	Uterine tube	The tubes extend from the ovaries to the body of the uterus in the fundus area.
		The egg is normally fertilized at the distal 2/3 of the uterine tube. This position is about 1 or 2 days after ovulation. Upon fertilization, the egg will continue to the uterus. It takes about a week for the fertilized egg to reach the endometrial lining.
3	Endometrial lining	The fertilized egg will implant in the endometrial lining.

There are numerous ligaments of the uterus that help anchor the uterus and ovaries in position.

Table 8C-3   Ligaments of the Uterus and Ovaries

	Reproductive structure	Description of the location
1	**Broad ligament**	Extends from the wall of the pelvic cavity on one side to the uterus (where it "splits" to form over the anterior side and posterior side of the uterus) to the other edge of the pelvic cavity. It completely envelopes the uterus.
	The broad ligament is made of three main regions: mesovarium, mesometrium, and the mesosalpinx.	
	Mesometrium: This is the portion that extends inferior to the uterine tube and ovary and connects to the lateral edge of the uterus. **Mesovarium:** This is the portion that extends from the ovary to the uterine tubes and envelopes the ovaries. **Mesosalpinx:** This is the portion that envelopes uterine tubes.	
2	**Uterosacral ligament**	Extends from the uterus to the anterior face of the sacrum.
3	**Round ligament**	Extends from the uterus (in the uterine tube area) to the external genitalia.
4	**Cardinal ligament**	Extends from the base of the uterus and vagina to the walls of the pelvis.
5	**Suspensory ligament**	Extends from the lateral edge of the ovary to the pelvic wall.
6	**Ovarian ligament**	Extends from the medial edge of the ovary to the uterus (about the area of the uterine tubes).

Table 8C-4 lists additional structures associated with the female reproductive system.

Table 8C-4   The Uterus and Vagina

	Reproductive structure	Description of the location
1	**Fundus**	This is the superior, rounded edge of the uterus.
2	**Cervix**	This is the narrowed region that leads to the vagina.
3	**External os**	Opening into the uterus.
4	**Perimetrium**	Outside lining of the uterus
5	**Myometrium**	Muscular portion of the uterus.
6	**Endometrium**	Inside lining of the uterus. This section enlarges (thickens) to prepare the uterus for the implantation of a fertilized egg.
7	**Vagina**	This is the birth canal.

CHAPTER 9   THE CRANIAL NERVES

All nerves of the body are important but the cranial nerves typically receive special attention because of their connection to the brain. There are twelve pairs of cranial nerves associated with the inferior side of the brain. These nerves are numbered with Roman numerals to designate their position on the brain. They are numbered in sequence from anterior to posterior. The cranial nerves are also designated by name.

Some of the nerves have afferent fibers that carry impulses from the periphery of the body to the brain. These are known as sensory nerves. Some nerves have efferent fibers that carry impulses from the brain out to the periphery of the body. These are known as motor nerves. Some of the cranial nerves consist of both afferent and efferent nerves. These are known as mixed nerves.

Cranial nerve I (CN I) connects to the temporal lobe of the brain and cranial nerve II (CN II) connects to the occipital lobe of the brain. Cranial nerves III through XII (CN III through CN XII) are associated with the brain stem.

Table 9-1 lists the cranial nerves in sequence with a brief function.

EXERCISE 9-1: IDENTIFICATION AND FUNCTION OF CRANIAL NERVES

Table 9-1   Cranial Nerves

Nerve Number	Nerve name	Nerve classification	Nerve Function
I	Olfactory	Sensory	Senses smell
II	Optic	Sensory	Detects vision
III	Oculomotor	Motor	Controls eye muscle for eye movement Controls focusing the lens Controls pupil constriction
IV	Trochlear	Motor	Controls superior oblique muscle
V	Trigeminal	Mixed	Detects head and face sensations Controls chewing movements
VI	Abducens	Motor	Controls lateral rectus muscle
VII	Facial	Mixed	Detects taste Allows facial expressions
VIII	Vestibulocochlear	Sensory	Senses balance Senses sound
IX	Glossopharyngeal	Mixed	Controls muscles for swallowing Detects tongue sensations
X	Vagus	Mixed	Detects thoracic and abdominal organ sensations Controls thoracic and abdominal movements
XI	Spinal accessory	Motor	Controls trapezius and sternocleidomastoid.
XII	Hypoglossal	Motor	Controls tongue movement

EXERCISE 9-2: CRANIAL NERVE REFLEXES

The following reflex tests will allow you to evaluate cranial nerve function. Keep in mind, definitive diagnosis cannot be determined by any single nerve abnormality. Once an abnormality is detected, the physician will order more extensive tests to make the proper diagnosis.

Some of the following tests are not exactly as they are in the hospital. We have added a bit to some of the tests to make them more fun. To perform this exercise, you will need to work with a partner.

Table 9-2 gives the instructions to perform the tests.

Table 9-2   Cranial Nerve Tests

Nerve	Test	Normal Response
CN I	Have your patient determine if they can detect different odors from 3 different containers.	The patient should be able to determine that there are at least 2 different odors from 2 of the 3 containers.
CN II	Have your patient stand 20 feet from the Snellen Eye Chart. Have your patient cover one eye. Determine which line on the chart your patient was able to read without any errors. The numbers on the chart mean this: The top number is always 20. The bottom number is what the patient is rated at. For example: If a patient has a rating of 20/25, this means: what the patient can see at 20 feet, other people can see the same thing at 25 feet.	Normal vision is 20/20. Vision rated at 20/15 is better. Vision rated at 20/30 is not as good.

Table 9-2   Cranial Nerve Tests   (continued)

Nerve	Test	Normal Response
CN III	Have your patient follow a penlight with their eyes. Move the penlight up and down. They are to keep their head stationary. Pass the penlight in front of the patient's eye and observe the pupil.	The patient should be able to follow the penlight since this nerve controls the superior and inferior rectus muscle. The pupil should constrict when exposed to the light and constrict when the light moves away from the pupil.
CN IV	Have your patient follow a penlight with their eyes. Move the penlight laterally and downward. They are to keep their head stationary.	The patient should be able to follow the penlight since this nerve controls the superior oblique muscle.
CN V	Have your patient clench their teeth. Hold your hand under their chin and observe if your patient can at least partially open their jaw against the resistance. Have your patient close their eye. Rub a piece of cotton over the patient's mandible area. Rub a piece of cotton over the patient's maxillary area. Rub a piece of cotton over the patient's forehead area.	The patient should be able to overcome the resistance while opening their jaw. The mandibular portion of the trigeminal passes from the zygomatic area down the ramus of the mandible. The maxillary portion of the trigeminal passes from the zygomatic area to the bridge of the nose. The ophthalmic portion of the trigeminal passes from the zygomatic to the skin of the forehead.

Table 9-2   Cranial Nerve Tests   (continued)

Nerve	Test	Normal Response
CN VI	Have your patient follow a penlight with their eyes. Move the penlight laterally. They are to keep their head stationary.	Your patient should be able to follow the light going side to side. The abducens nerve controls the lateral rectus muscles.
CN VII	Have your patient raise their eyebrows. Have your patient puff out their cheeks

Touch the tip of your patient's tongue with a Q-tip® that has been dipped in a salt solution. Use the other end of the Q-tip® to dip into a sugar solution. Be careful to NOT double dip. | Your patient should be able to raise their eyebrows evenly and puff both cheeks out evenly.

Your patient should be able to distinguish salt and sugar. |
| **CN VIII** | One of the tests that can be performed is the following: Turn your patient on a revolving chair for 10 revolutions (not fast but not slow). After the last revolution, stop the rotation and quickly observe the movement of their eyes. | The patient's eyes should be moving back and forth fairly rapid. This is known as nystagmatism. This is normal. If nystagmatism occurs without revolution, a problem may exist. |
| **CN IX** | Place the bell of a stethoscope slightly lateral to the trachea and esophagus in the neck region. Have your patient chew and swallow a cracker. Listen for the sound of the cracker going down the esophagus.

Another test would be to test for the gag reflex. I suggest we don't do this because it's not fun. | Your patient should be able to swallow just fine. You should be able to hear the cracker going down the esophagus. |

Table 9-2   Cranial Nerve Tests   (continued)

Nerve	Test	Normal Response
CN X	Place the bell of the stethoscope slightly to the left of the xiphoid process. This is the location of the esophagus entering the stomach. Have your patient swallow a cracker. You should hear the cracker "plopping" into the stomach. Repeat this by having your patient swallow 3 gulps of water.	The vagus nerve also controls the movement of food down the esophagus. This process is called peristalsis. You should be able to hear 3 individual gulps of water as it enters the stomach.
CN XI	Put your hands on your patient's shoulders. Apply a little pressure and have your patient shrug their shoulders. Put your hands on the side of your patient's head. Apply a little pressure and have your patient try to move their head side to side.	Your patient should be able to shrug their shoulders evenly. Your patient should be able to move their head side to side against the resistance.
CN XII	Have your patient stick out their tongue	Their tongue should come out straight and not off to the left or the right.

CHAPTER 10   THE EAR

The ear is a specialized structure of the nervous system just as the eyes are. Most people are very well aware that the ear is involved in hearing. However, the ear is also involved in balance. We will discuss the hearing process and the structures involved in hearing first.

Sound waves enter into the ear canal. The sound waves will cause the **tympanum** to vibrate. The tympanum will vibrate the **malleus, incus,** and **stapes.** The stapes causes the **oval window** (a membrane portion of the cochlea) to vibrate.   This vibration will set into motion the fluid that is found inside the **cochlea.**   The movement of this fluid will activate various cells associated with the **organ of Corti**, which is located in the cochlea. There are nerves that will emerge from the organ of Corti and enter into the temporal lobe of the brain for interpretation.

If a person has a middle ear infection, the infection may hinder the movement of the *ossicles*. This inhibition will result in abnormal movement of the oval window and therefore abnormal movement of the fluid in the cochlea. This may result in an abnormal signal begin sent to the brain for interpretation.

The ear is also involved in balance. Located in the inner ear, next to the cochlea, are three tubes called the **semicircular canals**. These canals contain a fluid that moves with the motions of the body. As the body moves, the fluid in the semicircular canals will move and will therefore activate nerve cells that send a message to the brain. The brain will then interpret the motion of the body.

Most people are familiar with getting dizzy as we spin around. As we spin around, the fluid in the semicircular canals will move. This fluid motion will activate nerve cells and the brain interprets the direction we are spinning. When we stop, the fluid continues to move. This gives the impression that we are still moving. Then, the fluid stops and begins to move in the opposite direction all the while we are trying to stand still. All of a sudden, our brain interprets motion in the opposite direction. Then, the fluid rocks back the other way. Our brain quickly interprets motion in the other direction. This continues for a while until the fluid stops rocking back and forth. Until the fluid stops, the brain is receiving a constant influx of confusing messages in reference to the direction the body is moving even though the body isn't moving at all!

While studying the table below, examine figure 10-1. Most textbooks do not have a picture of the external ear.

Table 10-1   The External Ear

1	Pinna	This is the entire outer ear. Sometimes called the auricle.
2	Helix	This is the outer rim of the ear.
3	Antihelix	This is the smaller rim that parallels the helix. This is closer to the external auditory canal.
4	Crus of the Helix	This is a ridge that parallels the antihelix. This is even closer to the external auditory canal.
5	Scapha	This is the depression located under the rim of the ear
6	Antitragus	Put your finger on the antihelix. Go inferior until you feel a bump. This is the antitragus.
7	Tragus	Opposite the antitragus is the tragus. This is the cartilage tissue many push in to block sound.
8	Intertragic notch	Put your finger between the tragus and antitragus. Move your finger downward into the slot. This slot is the intertragic notch.
9	Triangular fossa	This is the depression that is superior to the antihelix
10	Cymba	This is the depression between the crus of the helix and the antihelix. It is also the depression inferior to the crus of the helix.
11	External auditory canal	This is the ear canal. Also called the external acoustic meatus.
12	Ear lobe	This is the inferior tissue of the pinna. Some people have "free" ear lobes and some have "fixed" ear lobes.

The dots on the ear correspond to the structures listed in the previous table. The ear lobe is not shown on this figure.

Figure 10-1 The External Ear

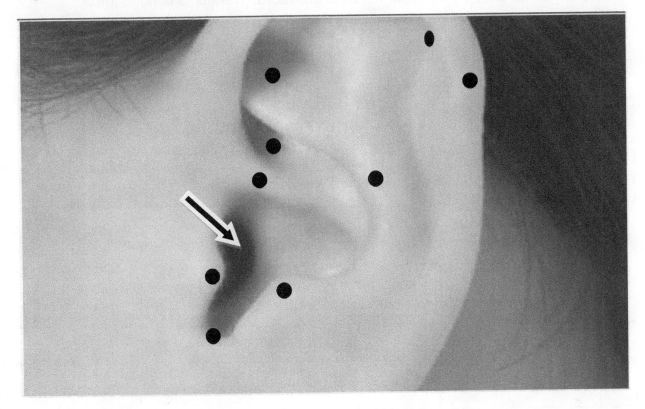

EXERCISE 10-2: HEARING

Table 10-2 lists the anatomical structures of the ear to be studied in this class. The best way to study the ear structures is to follow sound waves through the ear canal until the cochlear nerve is activated. The ear is divided into: outer ear, middle ear, and inner ear.

Table 10-2   Hearing

OUTER EAR		
1	**Pinna**	The pinna is the outer ear. It is designed to collect sound waves and "funnel" the waves toward the external auditory canal.
2	**External auditory canal**	Also called the **external auditory meatus**. Sound waves travel through this canal toward the eardrum.
3	**Tympanic membrane**	Also called the **tympanum**. Sound waves will cause the tympanum to vibrate.
MIDDLE EAR		
4	**Malleus**	The malleus is the first ossicle to vibrate.
5	**Incus**	The incus is the second ossicle to vibrate.
6	**Stapes**	The stapes is the third ossicle to vibrate. The stapes is connected to a membrane covering the oval window.
7	**Oval window**	This is an opening into the cochlea of the ear.
INNER EAR		
8	**Cochlea**	The vibration of the oval window membrane causes the vibration of fluid in the cochlea, which stimulates special cells that are involved in hearing.

Table 10-3   Balance

INNER EAR		
1	**Vestibular complex**	This complex is made of the **vestibular apparatus** and the **semicircular canals**.
Upon motion of the body, fluid within the vestibular complex moves in such a manner to stimulate special cells. These cells send signals to the brain for the interpretation of balance and equilibrium.		

Table 10-4   Other Structures Associated with the Ear

1	**Tympanic cavity**	This is the area between the tympanum and the cochlea.
2	**Pharyngotympanic tube**	Also called the auditory tube. This tube extends from the middle ear to the nasopharynx region. It aids to maintain pressure equilibrium within the middle ear.
3	**Vestibulocochlear nerve**	This nerve transmits information from the cochlea and the vestibular complex to the brain for interpretation of hearing and balance. This is known as cranial nerve VIII.
4	**Petrous portion of the temporal bone**	The vestibular complex and cochlea are inside this bony structure for protection.

PRONUNCIATION

1	Antihelix (an-tee-hee-licks)	11	Nasopharynx (nay-zoe-far-inks)
2	Antitragus (an-tee-tray-gus)	12	Ossicles (ah-si-kuls)
3	Cochlea (kok-lee-uh)	13	Petrous (peh-trus)
4	Crus (krus)	14	Pharyngotympanic (fuh-ring-go-tim-panik)
5	Cymba (sim-buh)	15	Scapha (skaa-fuh)
6	Helix (hee-licks)	16	Stapes (stay-peez)
7	Incus (ing-kus)	17	Tragus (tray-gus)
8	Intertragic (in-ter-traa-jik)	18	Tympanic (tim-paa-nik)
9	Malleus (muh-lee-us)	19	Vestibulocochlear (ves-tib-you-loe-kok-lee-ar)
10	Meatus (mee-ay-tus)		

CHAPTER 11   THE EYES

Most of the senses of the body can be placed into five major categories. Those five categories are, taste, sight, hearing, touch, and smell. There are specialized structures that are involved with the function of each of these senses. In this course, we will limit our discussion to the eyes and ears.

Six muscles control each eye. One interesting thing concerning the muscles of the eyes is the fact that when the medial rectus muscle of the left eye contracts, the lateral rectus muscle of the right eye contracts. When this occurs, both eyes will be looking to the right.

The part of the eye that is involved in vision is called the **retina**. The retina consists of two primary cell types called *rods* and *cones*. The cones operate during bright light conditions (daylight). They send impulses to the occipital lobe of the brain for the interpretation of color vision. The rods can operate during dim light conditions but do not detect color. The rods and cones will be activated by light (dim light is adequate for rods but bright light is needed to activate the cones). Once activated, they will send impulses through a series of nerves to the **optic nerve**, which is located in the **optic disc** area. Because of the location of the optic nerve and blood vessels in the optic disc area, there isn't any room for any rods or cones in that area. Therefore, this area is also known as the "*blind spot*" area. Nerve impulses will travel along the optic nerve to the occipital lobe of the brain. It is in the occipital lobe where vision is interpreted.

In order to activate the rods or cones, light must strike an object, bounce off that object, and enter through the **sclera** and into the **anterior chamber**. The light image continues to pass through the **pupil** and through the **lens**. The lens will then focus the object onto the retina. If the light image passes through the lens to the center back of the eye, the image will be focused on the **fovea centralis** of the retina. The fovea centralis contains only cones, no rods. Since there are only cones present in the fovea centralis, the image that is focused on this area turns out to be the sharpest, clearest image. Any light image that is focused on the periphery of the retina won't be as sharp or clear because the periphery consists of a mixture of rods and cones.

The lens can change its shape in order to focus the image on the retina properly by the action of **suspensory ligaments** that are attached to **ciliary bodies**.

The **cornea** of the eye is actually modified sclera. The cornea is constantly exposed to the dry environment. Because of the exposure, the cornea can become very dehydrated. To prevent this dehydration, the eye is continually lubricated. The lubrication fluid comes from the **lacrimal gland**. This gland is located at the lateral-superior portion of the eye. Tears from the lacrimal gland are swept across the eye and drain from the eye into the lacrimal foramen. Excessive tears, as in the case of crying, will flow from the eye to the surface of the face and also into the lacrimal foramen and drain into the nose. This will cause the nose to "run".

EXERCISE 11-1: EXTRAOCULAR MUSCLES

While studying the table below, examine figures in your textbook.

Table 11-1   The Extraocular Muscles

	Description	Eye Muscle	Function
1	The most lateral muscle of the eye	lateral rectus m.	Causes the right eye to rotate to the right. Causes the left eye to rotate to the left.
2	The most medial muscle of the eye	medial rectus m.	Causes the right eye to rotate to the left. Causes the left eye to rotate to the right.
3	The most superior muscle of the eye	superior rectus m.	Causes the eye to rotate upward.
4	The most inferior muscle of the eye	inferior rectus m.	Causes the eye to rotate downward.
5	This muscle connects to the superior, posterior portion of the eye and passes through a "pulley" system near the medial aspect of the eye socket.	superior oblique m.	Pulls the posterior portion of the eye upward causing the anterior portion of the eye to roll downward and lateral.
6	This muscle connects to the inferior, posterior portion of the eye and is near the lateral aspect of the eye socket.	inferior oblique m.	Pulls the bottom of the eye forward causing the eye to roll upward and to the side.
7	The "pulley" system located nearest the medial portion of the eye socket	trochlea	Acts as a pulley system for the superior oblique muscle.

Also identify the nasal bone, frontal bone, and maxillary bone.

EXERCISE 11-2: THE ANATOMY OF THE EYE

Using figures in your textbook, study the internal components of the eye by following the pathway of light through the eye. Use table 11-2 to help you follow that path of light to the retina of the eye. In order to see anything, light must reflect off the object and pass through the eye to the retina.

Table 11-2   The Pathway of Light Through the Eye

1	Sclera	This is the "white" of the eye. The anterior portion of the sclera is the cornea, which is transparent. The cornea is modified sclera.
2	Cornea	Light passes through the cornea.
3	Anterior chamber	Light passes through the anterior chamber that consists of **aqueous humor**. This area is anterior to the iris.
4	Pupil	The pupil is an opening through the iris.
5	Iris	This tissue gives the eye its color.
6	Posterior chamber	Light passes through the posterior chamber, which also consists of aqueous humor. This area is posterior to the iris.
The anterior chamber and posterior chamber make up the anterior cavity.		
7	Lens	The lens is designed to focus the object on the retina of the eye.
8	Posterior cavity	Light passes through the largest portion of the eye. This cavity is filled with a jelly-like substance called the **vitreous body**. Sometimes, this area is called the **vitreous chamber**.
9	Retina	Light rays are focused on some aspect of the retina.

EXERCISE 11-3: THE RETINA

Table 11-3   Details of the Retina

1	**Fovea**	Also called the fovea centralis. This is an area located in the retina at a point that is central to the lens of the eye. This area consists of 100% cones.
2	**Cones**	These are photoreceptor cells of the retina that detect color vision. In order for these cells to be activated, bright light is required.
3	**Rods**	These are specialized cells of the retina that are able to function in dim light. These cells do not differentiate color.
4	**Optic disc**	This is the area of the eye where blood vessels enter and exit and the optic nerve exits the eye. This area is void of rods and cones. Due to the lack of rods and cones, sometimes this area is called the "blind spot." This area is located a bit medial to the center of the back of the eye.

EXERCISE 11-4: THE BLIND SPOT

Photoreceptors are not present in the optic disc area. Therefore, this is known as the blind spot. Follow the instructions below to help you determine that the blind spot really exists.

1. Close your left eye and hold figure 11-1 away from your face at a distance of your outstretched arm. You will need to turn the figure in such a manner so the dot is on the right side.

2. Using your right eye, focus on the plus (+) symbol. You should be able to see the plus symbol and the dot but be sure to focus on the plus symbol.

3. Move the image closer to your face while you continue to stare at the plus symbol.

4. Pretty soon, you will see the dot disappear.

5. When the dot disappears, that means the dot image has been focused on the blind spot. You will not be able to see it. You should still be able to see the plus symbol.

6. You can move the figure up or down or to the side and the dot will reappear.

7. Now, you can do the same for the other eye.

Figure 11-1   Visual Demonstration of the Blind Spot

Exercise 11-5: Demonstration of the Fovea (Fovea Centralis)

The fovea does not consist of rods. It only consists of cones, which only function under bright light conditions.

1. Go outside at night at stare straight at a star. The star is so far away that its light will actually appear dim to us.

   By staring straight at the star, the image of the star will focus on the fovea centralis. The star seems to "disappear".

2. While continuing to stare at the star, turn your head to the right or left just a bit.

   The star will "reappear". The image of the star will now be focused on a peripheral region of the retina. The peripheral region of the retina consists of a combination of rods and cones. As the image of the star is focused on a peripheral rod, the rod is activated and an impulse is sent to the occipital lobe of the brain.

EXERCISE 11-6: ADDITIONAL STRUCTURES OF THE EYE

Table 11-4   Other Structures of the Eye

1	**Suspensory ligaments**	These ligaments extend from the ciliary bodies to the lens.
2	**Ciliary bodies**	Ciliary bodies are near the junction of the sclera and the cornea. They are an extension of the choroid, which is one of the layers of the internal eye. The ciliary bodies consist of ciliary muscles.
	The ciliary muscles will contract and relax thus changing the shape of the lens for focusing purposes.	

Table 11-5   Structures of the External Eye

1	**Medial and Lateral Canthus**	These are the areas of the eye where the upper and lower eyelids connect together.
2	**Lacrimal caruncle**	Located in the area of the medial canthus. The cells of the lacrimal caruncle produce thick secretions.
3	**Palpebrae**	This is the term in reference to the eyelids.
4	**Lacrimal gland**	This gland produces the tears. It is located on the superior, lateral portion of the eye socket.
5	**Nasolacrimal duct**	Tears flow across the eye to the nasolacrimal duct. Tears flow through the lacrimal foramen, into the duct, which leads to the nasal cavity.

PRONUNCIATION

1	Aqueous (ah-kwee-us)	9	Nasolacrimal (nay-zoe-lak-ri-mul)
2	Canthus (kan-thus)	10	Oblique (oh-bleek)
3	Caruncle (kar-ung-kul)	11	Palpebrae (pal-puh-bree)
4	Cornea (kor-nee-uh)	12	Presbyopia (prez-bee-oh-pee-uh)
5	Fovea centralis (foe-vee-uh sen-tral-is)	13	Retina (ret-i-nuh)
6	Glaucoma (glaw-koe-muh)	14	Sclera (sklare-uh)
7	Lacrimal (lak-ri-mul)	15	Trochlea (trok-lee-uh)
8	Myopia (mie-oh-pee-uh)	16	Vitreous (vit-ree-us)

Name _____

CHAPTER 1   ANATOMICAL TERMINOLOGY   ASSIGNMENT

1. The cubital area is located _____ to the antecubital area.

2. The right nipple area is _____ and _____ to the umbilical (use two terms).

3. The popliteal area is located _____ to the patella area.

4. The hallux is located _____ to the little toe.

5. In the anatomical position, the palms face _____.

6. A dissectional cut that starts 8 cm above the elbow (on the lateral side) and angles down the arm to a point 2 cm above the elbow (on the medial side) would be a/an _____ cut.

7. The fundus of the liver is located in the _____ abdominopelvic area.

8. What is the anatomical name for the posterior aspect of the knee?

9. What is the anatomical name for the lower arm?

10. Our ears are on the _____ side of our face.

CHAPTER 2   CELLS AND TISSUES   ASSIGNMENT

1. Identify a typical cell type that would be found lining most of the trachea.

2. Identify the type of tissue that consists of mainly parallel fibers, which create tremendous strength. (be more specific than "connective.")

3. Identify the main tissue type that provides a lot of cushion and insulation around the organs of the body. (Be more specific than "connective").

4. Identify the two types of cells that sit in a lacuna.

5. Identify the type of cell that is involved in labor contractions during child birth.

6. What is the hollow space of a tube in which fluid flows, such as the hollow space of a urinary tube or the hollow space of a garden hose called?

7. What do the following prefixes mean? ("leuko" and "erythro")

8. What does this suffix mean: "cyte"?

9. Identify the cells that are anucleated.

10. Identify the cells that are multinucleated.

CHAPTER 3   OVERVIEW OF THE REGIONS   ASSIGNMENT

1. Within which region of long bones can we find red marrow?

2. Within which region of long bones can we find yellow marrow?

3. When we say that a child has broken their growth plate or they have broken their growth zone, what region of the bone has been broken?

4. When a muscle contracts, which myofilament moves or slides?

5. When the temperature outside is cold, the blood vessels will constrict in an effort to conserve heat. When the temperature outside is warm, the blood vessels will dilate in an effort to lose heat so we stay cooler. Which layer of the blood vessels is responsible for these actions?

6. Which part of a neuron is typically the longest of all the neuron parts?

7. When you are looking at a slide of an artery and a vein that are side by side, how can you tell which one is the artery and which one is the vein?

8. A sarcomere consists of the length from one Z disk to the other Z disk. Which of the following is the correct sequence of the "bands" between one Z disk and the other Z disk?
    a.   Z A I A Z
    b.   Z I A I Z
    c.   Z I A H Z
    d.   Z H I H Z

9. What is the Latin meaning of the word, "soma?"

10. What is the meaning of the word, "lumen?"

Name _____

CHAPTER 4A   SKULL BONES AND BONE STRUCTURES   ASSIGNMENT

1. Name the largest foramen that is lateral to the foramen lacerum from the inferior view.

2. How many sphenoid bones are in the skull?

3. Name the bone that makes up the inferior portion of the nasal septum.

4. Name the bone that is anterior to the ethmoid bone within the eye socket.

5. The mastoid process is not a separate bone. It is a process that is part of which skull bone?

6. Name the foramen (canals) that are superior to the occipital condyles. Remember to study everything in the anatomical position.

7. The foramen magnum is a huge hole in what major skull bone?

8. The anterior palatine is actually a process of what major facial bone?

9. The clivus is a process of two major bones. What are they?

10. The mandibular fossa is a depression associated with what major skull bone?

Name _____

CHAPTER 4B   HEAD AND NECK   SKELETAL MUSCLES   ASSIGNMENT

1. Name the muscle of the neck region that has to be removed in order to see deeper muscles such as the sternocleidomastoid.

2. Identify the muscle that attaches to the clavicle, the scapula, and the mastoid process.

3. Which is the most of superior muscle of the two listed: zygomaticus major or zygomaticus minor?

4. Identify two muscles that are attached to the hyoid bone.

5. Identify the muscle that is immediately lateral to the mentalis.

6. Identify the major muscle involved in closing the jaw that is located on the lateral side of the face.

7. Name the muscle located between the nasalis and the levator labii superioris muscle.

8. Name the muscle located between the levator scapulae and the middle scalene muscle.

9. Identify the dense tissue that connects the frontalis with the occipitalis.

10. Name the most superficial muscle of the anterior neck region.

Name _____

CHAPTER 4C   HEAD AND NECK   BLOOD VESSELS   ASSIGNMENT

1. The right common carotid artery is a branch off the _____ artery (trunk).

2. The left common carotid artery branches off the _____

3. Which blood vessel eventually leads to the cerebral arterial circle; internal carotid or external carotid?

4. The right jugular vein and the right subclavian vein join to form the right _____ vein.

5. What artery passes through the transverse foramen of the cervical vertebrae?

6. The facial artery goes across the body of the mandible just a few centimeters anterior to the _____ muscle.

7. The facial vein drains into the internal jugular vein or the external jugular vein?

8. Which is larger in diameter, the internal jugular vein or the external jugular vein?

9. The vertebral arteries branch off the _____ arteries.

10. The occipital artery and the facial artery are branches off the _____ artery.

Name _____

<u>Chapter 4D   Head and Neck Nerves</u>   <u>The Brain   Assignment</u>

1. The left hemisphere and the right hemisphere must coordinate their functions with each other. What brain structure allows for this communication?

2. What is the anatomical name for the pituitary gland?

3. What does the choroid plexus produce?

4. Identify the meninges from the brain tissue to the inside lining of the skull.

5. Name the parts of the corpus callosum beginning with the rostrum and going all the way to the most posterior portion (in sequence).

6. Identify two brain regions that make up the diencephalon.

7. The thalamus consists of which of the four ventricles?

8. What is the name of the stalk that connects the pituitary gland to the hypothalamus?

9. The posterior portion of the midbrain consists of two small bumps (bulges), which are collectively called _____.

10. What causes hydrocephalic conditions? Answer needs to use terminology studied in this chapter.

CHAPTER 5A   UPPER APPENDICULAR   SKELETON   ASSIGNMENT

1. Identify the most medial structure of the clavicle.

2. The head of the humerus pivots in what structure of the scapula?

3. Which is an anterior structure: olecranon fossa or coronoid fossa?

4. Which condyle pivots with the radius?

5. Describe the location of the trochlear notch.

6. Which part of the ulna pivots on the trochlear condyle of the humerus?

7. Name the carpal bone that is medial to the capitate.

8. How many phalanges does the pollex have?

9. Identify digit number 1.

10. Describe how to determine the difference between the anterior side of the radius and the posterior side.

CHAPTER 5B   UPPER APPENDICULAR   SKELETAL MUSCLES   ASSIGNMENT

1. Are the flexors of the antebrachium anterior or posterior muscles?

2. The short head of the biceps brachii originates on what bony structure of the scapula?

3. The tendon of what muscle (be specific) passes through the intertubercular sulcus of the humerus?

4. Which portion of the triceps brachii originates on the lateral border of the scapula?

5. The coracobrachialis muscle originates on what bony structure of the scapula?

6. What is the most lateral muscle of the antebrachium?

7. What muscle lies deep to the tendon of the palmaris longus muscle?

8. Name a muscle that lies between the extensor digitorum and the extensor carpi ulnaris.

9. Which muscle is more superior to the other of the ones listed: extensor pollicis longus or the abductor pollicis longus?

10. What is the name of the tendinous material found between and connecting the hypothenar muscles with the thenar muscles?

Name _____

<u>CHAPTER 5C</u>   <u>UPPER APPENDICULAR</u>   <u>BLOOD VESSELS</u>   <u>ASSIGNMENT</u>

1. The brachial artery runs along the medial side, anterior side, or lateral side of the humerus?

2. The median cubital vein is located in what anatomical region of the arm?

3. The cephalic vein in the antebrachial region does which of the following: it begins on the anterior side and goes posterior or it begins on the posterior side and goes anterior?

4. The median cubital vein merges with the; cephalic vein or basilic vein?

5. Which is more superficial; the radial vein or the cephalic vein?

6. The basilic vein in the antebrachial region does which of the following: it begins on the anterior side and goes posterior or it begins on the posterior side and goes anterior?

7. The circumflex artery of the humerus is nearest the; proximal end or distal end?

8. The cephalic vein forms the; axillary vein, subclavian vein, or the basilic vein?

9. The basilic vein forms the; axillary vein, subclavian vein, or the cephalic vein?

10. The interosseus artery than goes through the center of the interosseous membrane of the antebrachium, arises from the; ulnar artery or the radial artery?

Name _____

1. Which of the following nerves run near the lateral epicondyle of the humerus; ulnar nerve, radial nerve or median nerve?

2. Which of the following nerves run near the medial epicondyle of the humerus; ulnar nerve, radial nerve or median nerve?

3. Which of the following nerves run near the coronoid fossa of the humerus; ulnar nerve, radial nerve or median nerve?

4. Branches from the _____ nerve innervate digits II through IV on the anterior side.

5. Branches from the _____ nerve innervate digits I through III on the posterior side.

6. There are many places in the body where the arteries, veins, and nerves run parallel to each other. Many times, they run in this manner: vein – artery – nerve. This creates the acronym VAN. In the upper limb, what nerve is involved with this acronym; radial nerve, ulnar nerve, or median nerve?

7. The ulnar nerve arises from the brachial plexus. It originates from the spinal nerve that is closest to which of the following vertebrae: C5,C7, or T1?

8. The radial nerve arises from the brachial plexus. It originates from the spinal nerve that is closest to which of the following vertebrae: C5,C7, or T1?

9. The musculocutaneous nerve is closely related to which of the following nerves: radial nerve, ulnar nerve, or median nerve?

10. Which of the following nerves is bumped, giving the feeling (in layman's terms) that you hit your "funny bone?" (radial nerve, ulnar nerve, or the median nerve).

Name _____

<u>C</u>HAPTER 6A   <u>L</u>OWER <u>A</u>PPENDICULAR   <u>S</u>KELETON   <u>A</u>SSIGNMENT

1. What part of the os coxa do you sit on?

2. What structure of the femur fits in the acetabular fossa?

3. Which is superior to the other: the greater sciatic notch or the lesser sciatic notch?

4. The tibia pivots on which tarsal?

5. The pelvic outlet spans the distance between the _____ of the left and right os coxa.

6. a. which has a larger public angle (male or female)?
   b. which has a larger pelvic outlet (male or female)?

7. The coccyx is formed from how many fused bones?

8. Each os coxa is made of what three bones?

9. The intercondylar eminence of the tibia is made of two projections. What is the name of those projections?

10. Identify the large, lateral, proximal bulge of the femur.

Name _____

1. Are the hamstrings anterior or posterior muscles?

2. Are the quadriceps anterior or posterior muscles?

3. The iliopsoas muscle inserts on what part of the femur?

4. Which of the following muscles is nearest the proximal portion of the gracilis muscles; iliopsoas, pectineus, or adductor longus?

5. Which of the following muscles is nearest the proximal portion of the sartorius muscle; iliopsoas, pectineus, or adductor longus?

6. Which of the following is on the anterior side of the gracilis muscle; adductor longus or adductor magnus?

7. The semimembranosus is deep to which posterior thigh muscle?

8. The gastrocnemius muscle inserts on the calcaneus via the _____ tendon.

9. The fibularis longus has a tendon that loops around the _____ and extends to the little toe.

10. Which of the following is true of the tibialis anterior; it originates a little bit lateral and crosses over the tibial bone to insert on a medial toe or it originates a little bit medial and crosses over the tibial bone to insert on a lateral toe.

Name _____

1. Name the two veins that join to form the popliteal vein.

2. Blood in the great saphenous vein enters into what vein next?

3. Blood in the femoral artery came from what blood vessel?

4. What is the name of the opening through the connective tissue that allows the femoral artery to form the popliteal artery?

5. The fibular artery branches off the anterior or the posterior tibial artery?

6. Of the two listed, which one is more lateral; femoral artery or femoral vein?

7. Of the two listed, which one is more medial; femoral vein or great saphenous vein?

8. The genicular arteries are located at the proximal or the distal end of the femur.

9. Which of the following is correct regarding the location of the opening for the anterior tibial artery; it is located between the fibula and the tibia at the proximal end or it is located between the fibula and tibia at the distal end?

10. Name the artery that passes between the medial and lateral condyles of the femur.

Name _____

1. The first nerve of the sacral plexus emerges from which of the following regions;
    L3, L4, L5, S1, or S2.

2. There are two parts to the sciatic nerve. Identify them.

3. The sciatic nerve runs along the anterior or the posterior side of the thigh?

4. The two parts of the sciatic nerve actually "splits" at the area of which region of
    the leg?

5. The femoral nerve arises from what plexus?

6. The genitofemoral nerve innervates the genitals. This nerve arises from what plexus?

7. The saphenous nerve arises from what plexus?

8. The obturator nerve passes through obturator foramen. What plexus does it arise from?

9. The pudendal nerve arises from what plexus?

10. The plexus is considered to be a part of the central nervous system or the peripheral nervous system?

CHAPTER 7A   TORSO REGION   SKELETON   ASSIGNMENT

1. Name the two pairs of bony structures that make up the neural arch. Or; Name the two pairs of bony structures that make up the walls of the vertebral foramen.

2. Which term is singular; vertebra or vertebrae?

3. What passes through the vertebral foramen?

4. What passes through the transverse foramen?

5. What portion of the spinal cord exits the sacral hiatus?

6. What is one structure that all cervical vertebrae have that other vertebrae do not have?

7. Which group of vertebrae supports the main weight of the body?

8. Can you tell if a skeleton is a female by counting the number of ribs present?

9. Which group of vertebrae do the ribs attach to?

10. Rib number 4 has articulation points with what two vertebrae?

Name _____

1. What is the trapezium and what is the trapezius?

2. Name the erector spinae muscles going from lateral to medial.

3. The anterior wall and posterior wall of the rectus sheath envelopes what abdominal muscle?

4. What is the name of the connective tissue that "divides" the segments of the rectus abdominis muscles?

5. The left rectus sheath and the right rectus sheath join in the middle of the abdomen forming a vertical white line. This is called the _____.

6. Identify the muscle that is associated with the thoracolumbar fascia.

7. Which muscle is more inferior to the other listed; teres major or teres minor?

8. Which muscle extends farther into the abdomen; iliacus or psoas major?

9. Which muscle is being described (internal intercostal or external intercostal): This muscle angles anteriorly from the superior rib to the inferior rib.

10. Identify the muscle that is deep to the internal oblique.

Name _____

<u>Chapter 7C$_1$</u>   <u>Torso Region</u>   <u>The Heart</u>   <u>Assignment</u>

1. The moderator band can be found in which chamber of the heart?

2. Chordae tendineae connect to two structures. Identify those structures.

3. Which side of the heart (left or right) is oxygenated?

4. Which contains deoxygenated blood; pulmonary arteries or pulmonary veins?

5. Which layer of the heart consists of the cardiac cells;
    epicardium, myocardium, or endocardium?

6. The two vena cavas enter into which chamber of the heart?

7. How can you tell if you are looking at a papillary muscle or trabeculae carneae?

8. The ductus ligamentum of the adult heart is the remnant of the _____ of the fetal heart.

9. Which side of the heart is the strongest pump?

10. Where is the heart's natural pacemaker located?

Name _____

CHAPTER 7C₂ TORSO REGION   THE BLOOD VESSELS   ASSIGNMENT

1. Which of the following is the most superior branch off the descending aorta after it passes through the diaphragm muscle?
    (inferior mesenteric a, superior mesenteric a, or the celiac a)

2. Blood returning from the abdominal organs flow in the ____ vein and enters into the liver before going into the inferior vena cava.

3. What type of muscle tissue makes up the tunica media layer of the blood vessels?

4. Name 3 branches that come off the celiac trunk (artery).

5. The gastroduodenal artery supplies the lesser curvature of the stomach or the greater curvature of the stomach?

6. The appendicular artery that supplies the appendix is a branch off the superior mesenteric or the inferior mesenteric artery?

7. The inferior vena cava lies on the right or left lateral of the abdominal aorta?

8. The hepatic veins enter or exit the inferior vena cava?

9. The jejunal and ilial arteries and veins are embedded in the mesentery or omentum?

10. The superior vena cava is formed from what two veins?

Name _____

1. The conus medullaris exists at approximately which vertebral level?

2. The cauda equina is mostly at which of the following vertebral levels?
    a. T10 through L3
    b. L1 through L5
    c. L1 through Co
    d. T10 through Co

3. The anterior portion of the spinal cord has how many arteries and the posterior portion of the spinal cord has how many arteries?

4. Which is a wider fissure; anterior median fissure (sulcus) or posterior median fissure (sulcus)?

5. Which root forms a bulge called the spinal ganglion: anterior root or posterior root?

6. A bulging disc between vertebrae C5 and C6 could result in a problem with which of the following?
   a. arm extension
   b. arm flexion
   c. wrist extension
   d. wrist flexion

7. A bulging disc between which vertebrae can result in a decreased knee jerk reflex?

8. The sympathetic nerves are associated with branches of the spinal cord in with of the following areas?
   a. cervical region and sacral region
   b. upper thoracic through the upper lumbar region
   c. upper thoracic through lower thoracic region
   d. lower thoracic through the sacral region

9. The parasympathetic nerves are associated with branches of the spinal cord in with of the following areas?
   a. cervical region and sacral region
   b. upper thoracic through the upper lumbar region
   c. upper thoracic through lower thoracic region
   d. lower thoracic through the sacral region

10. The denticulate ligaments are extensions of which meningeal layer?

Name _____

<u>CHAPTER 7E   THE TORSO   THE LUNGS   ASSIGNMENT</u>

1. There are some cells in the trachea that are involved in producing mucus, which helps to protect our lungs. What are these cells called?

2. Which lung has the cardiac notch?

3. Which primary bronchus angles inferiorly more (straighter into the lung) than the other?

4. What kind of cells make up the lining of the alveoli?

5. What is the name of the blood vessels that carry blood to the alveoli (pulmonary artery or pulmonary vein)?

6. In order to exhale, the diaphragm muscle must (go up or go down). When we exhale, is the diaphragm muscle contracting or relaxing?

7. What is the name of the area where the trachea branches to form the two primary bronchi?

8. The base of the lungs rest on the diaphragm muscle. This surface of the lungs is called the _____ surface.

9. What does it mean to have an upper respiratory infection?

10. Distinguish between asthma, bronchitis, and emphysema.

Name _____

<u>CHAPTER 7F   THE TORSO   ABDOMINAL ORGANS   ASSIGNMENT</u>

1. What is the name of the structure that closes the trachea in an effort to prevent choking when swallowing food?

2. What is the name of the first part of the large intestine?

3. What substances pass through the hepatopancreatic sphincter to enter into the duodenum?

4. What is the name of the muscular wave-like activity that pushes food through the digestive system?

5. Nutrients are absorbed through the _____ to enter into circulatory system to travel to all parts of the body.

6. What part of the pancreas is involved in producing enzymes for digestion in the small intestine?

7. What is the name of the longest part of the small intestine?

8. A good portion of the pancreas is located posterior to the ____.

9. Name the tubes in correct sequence as bile flows from the gallbladder to the duodenum.

10. Name the tubes in correct sequence as bile flows from the liver to the duodenum.

Name _____

CHAPTER 8A   PELVIC REGION   URINARY SYSTEM   ASSIGNMENT

1. What is the name of the tubes that pass through the renal pyramids to the minor calyces?

2. The ureters enter the urinary bladder. Do they enter the superior or inferior portion of the urinary bladder?

3. What is the name of the sphincter that we learned to control when we were "potty" trained as a toddler?

4. What is the name of the blood vessels that surround a cortical nephron?

5. Which kidney sits higher in the body?

6. Which kind of nephron (juxtamedullary or cortical) has most of its nephron loop in the renal pyramids?

7. What is the muscular portion of the urinary bladder called?

8. Blood in the interlobar arteriole will flow into what vessel next?

9. Describe the location of the interlobar arterioles.

10. Under normal circumstances, blood in the glomerular capillaries will enter into the efferent arteriole or the afferent arteriole.

Name _____

1. What does the sperm cell have that will propel it through the reproductive systems?

2. Which gland produces the most nutrients for the sperm cells?

3. What passes through the center of the corpora cavernosa and what passes through the center of the corpora spongiosum?

4. Sperm cells will enter into which part of the epididymis first?

5. What is the name of the tube that allows sperm cells to swim from the ductus deferens to the penile urethra?

6. Describe the location of the bulbo-urethral glands.

7. The bub of the penis is actually a part of what penile structure?

8. The ischiocavernosus muscles wraps around what structure of the penis?

9. There are 3 muscles that are collectively called the levator ani muscles. .These muscles make up the floor of the pelvic region. Name the muscles that are grouped as the levator ani muscles?

10. Describe the location of the scrotal and penile raphe.

Name _____

<u>CHAPTER 8C   PELVIC REGION   FEMALE REPRODUCTION   ASSIGNMENT</u>

1. What is inside the uterine tube that propels the egg toward the uterus?

2. The muscular portion of the uterus is made of smooth muscle and is responsible for uterine contractions. What is this muscular portion called?

3. Name 3 ligaments that help to anchor the uterus in position.

4. Name 3 ligaments that help to anchor the ovaries in position.

5. What part of the uterus is "shed" during menstruation?

6. Which is anterior in the standing position; the vagina or the urethra?

7. Describe the position of the uterus in relation to the urinary bladder.

8. What is the name of the portion of the broad ligament that is located between the uterine tubes and the ovarian ligament (ligament of the ovary)?

9. The mons pubis forms the labia majora or the labia minora?

10. There are 3 main layers of the uterus. Name them.

Name _____

1. Name all the cranial nerves that move the eyeball.

2. Name 3 cranial nerves that have the same name as the foramen or fissure or canal they pass through.

3. Bell's palsy is an inflammation of which of the cranial nerves?

4. Which portion of CN VIII is involved in balance?

5. Which cranial nerve is the most anterior of all the cranial nerves?

6. If activated, which cranial nerve will cause the heart rate to slow down?

7. When you bite your tongue, which cranial nerve will be activated?

8. There are actually 2 cranial nerves involved in taste. Name them.

9. In this lab activity, did you test the sensory or motor or both (mixed) reflexes of the trigeminal nerve?

10. Which cranial nerve controls the majority of muscles that move the eyeball?

Name _____

CHAPTER 10   THE EARS   ASSIGNMENT

1. The malleus, incus, and stapes are collectively called ____.

2. What structures make up the inner ear?

3. If there is blockage of the pharyngotympanic tube, pressure can build up in the tympanic cavity. This may cause the _____ to bulge laterally, thereby creating pain.

4. If the fluid inside the ____ moves back and forth, this may cause the patient to feel dizzy.

5. What structures are housed in the petrous portion of the temporal bone?

6. Identify two muscles in the middle ear that help to reduce the excess movement of some of the ossicles.

7. What is the name of the organ within the cochlea that, when stimulated, will send signals to the brain for the interpretation of hearing?

8. The stapes is attached to a membrane located at the entrance to the vestibular apparatus. What is this entrance called?

9. Describe Meniere's disease.

10. Which part of cranial nerve VIII is involved in balance?

Name _____

CHAPTER 11   THE EYES   ASSIGNMENT

1. What muscles must contract in order for a person to look "cross-eyed?" (be specific).

2. Name the muscle of the left eye and the muscle of the right eye that must contract to get a person to look to the left.

3. What does presbyopia and myopia mean?

4. What is the name of the chamber located between iris and the lens of the eye?

5. Contraction of smooth muscles in the _____ will cause a change in the diameter of the pupil.

6. Describe glaucoma (be sure to use "eye" terminology).

7. Describe "pink eye" (be sure to use "eye" terminology).

8. What muscle passes through the trochlea of the eye?

9. Explain the difference between the extraocular muscles and the intraocular muscles.

10. The sclera of the eye (white part of the eye) differentiates and forms the _____ of the eye.